Buckle Down!®

on CAHSEE

Mathematics

This book belongs to: _____

Buckle Down
Publishing

A Haights Cross Communications Company

Helping the schoolhouse meet the standards of the statehouse™

Acknowledgment

The High School Exit Exam Blueprint and the California Content Standards that appear within the Blueprint were developed by the California Department of Education.

Every effort has been made by the publisher to locate each owner of the copyrighted material reprinted in this publication and to secure the necessary permissions. If there are any questions regarding the use of these materials, the publisher will take appropriate corrective measures to acknowledge ownership in future publications.

ISBN 0-7836-2928-1

Catalog #1BD CA10CM 1   1 2 3 4 5 6 7 8 9 10

Editorial Director: John Hansen; Project Editor: Michael J. Morony; Editor: Paul Meyers; Production Editor: Michael Hankes; Production Director: Jennifer Booth; Production Supervisor: Ginny York; Art Director: Chris Wolf; Graphic Designer: Diane Hudachek.

Cover image: © Corbis

TABLE OF CONTENTS

Introduction

Buckle Down on CAHSEE Mathematics is designed to help you get your best score on the California High School Exit Exam in Mathematics. This is an important test that you must pass in order to get your high school diploma.

All of the lessons in this book are based on the standards and skills tested on the CAHSEE. In the course of this book, you'll review skills and strategies related to Number Sense, Algebra and Functions, Measurement and Geometry, Data Analysis and Probability, and Mathematical Reasoning. At the end of each lesson, you'll have an opportunity to "Test Your Skills" by answering multiple-choice questions similar to those you might see on the CAHSEE or other standardized tests in mathematics.

The CAHSEE requires that you have a lot of math knowledge and skills at your command. This book will help you to review, remember, or learn all you need to know to achieve your highest possible score on the test.

Testwise Strategies™

The best way to pass any math test is to learn and then practice the math. If you learn and practice the skills taught in this book, you will do your best on any math test. Here are a few tips to keep in mind on the day of a test.

Tip 1: Make sure you have your materials ready.

For most math tests, all you will need is two or three sharp pencils and an eraser. Some tests will allow you to use scratch paper and/or a calculator to work your problems. Your teacher will tell you what you need for a test. It is up to you to make sure your materials are ready to use.

Tip 2: Take a step-by-step approach to word problems.

Make sure you understand the question. Try to see the operation that is taking place. Pull the math from the problem. Reread the problem to make sure your math works. Do the math. Then, as always, check your work.

Tip 3: Learn to "plug in" answers to multiple-choice questions.

What if you are completely stumped on a multiple-choice question? What if your solution does not match any of the answer choices on a multiple-choice question? With practice, you will learn to "plug in" the answer choices until you find the right one.

Tip 4: DO NOT leave any questions blank.

Make sure you've answered every question, even if you are guessing. You might get it right!

Tip 5: Use all the test time given.

Use all the time that you have to work on the test. Do not stop working until the teacher tells you to do so. If you finish early, go back and check all your answers.

Tip 6: On test day, relax.

If you've learned and practiced the skills that are to be tested, you can relax, knowing that you're ready to do your best on any test.

Unit 1

Number Sense

The Golden Gate Bridge, at a length of 8,981 feet, is one of the world's longest suspension bridges. The coldest temperature recorded in California was $-45°F$ in Boca. The area of California is more than $4.1 \cdot 10^5 \text{ km}^2$. The population of Los Angeles is more than $3\frac{1}{2}$ million.

In order to work with facts like these, you need to use your number sense. Your brain gathers numbers in various forms and processes them to make them understandable. You also need to use your number sense to compare, contrast, or combine numbers.

In this unit, you will use your number sense in working with various concepts and representations of large and small numbers. You will perform the four operations of addition, subtraction, multiplication, and division on the various representations of numbers. You will also solve everyday consumer mathematics problems.

In This Unit

Number Concepts and Representation

Operations

Consumer Mathematics

Lesson 1: Number Concepts and Representation

Numbers can be expressed in a variety of ways. This lesson reviews some of the most common ways of expressing numbers.

Rational and Irrational Numbers

Rational numbers are numbers that can be expressed in fractional form, $\frac{a}{b}$, where a (the numerator) and b (the denominator) are both **integers** (counting numbers, their opposites, and zero) and $b \neq 0$. In decimal form, the rational numbers are either terminating or repeating decimals. A terminating decimal comes to a complete stop, whereas a repeating decimal continues the same digit or block of digits forever.

 Example

Here are some examples of rational numbers.

$$5 \qquad -\frac{3}{7} \qquad -4\frac{3}{11} \qquad -9.261 \qquad 0.6$$

Irrational numbers are numbers that cannot be expressed in fractional form using integers. In decimal form, the irrational numbers are nonterminating (never-ending), nonrepeating decimals.

 Example

Here are some examples of irrational numbers.

$$\pi \qquad \sqrt{2} \qquad 6\sqrt{5} \qquad -\frac{\sqrt{3}}{3} \qquad -4.6298215\ldots$$

 TIP: The rational numbers include the counting numbers, whole numbers, and integers. Together, the rational and irrational numbers make up the **real numbers**.

Practice

Directions: For Numbers 1 through 8, write whether the number is rational (R) or irrational (I).

1. 15.77 _____

2. $\sqrt{5}$ _____

3. $\frac{1}{6}$ _____

4. 81.6783 . . . _____

5. $\frac{45}{8}$ _____

6. −8.34 _____

7. 0.23984 . . . _____

8. 4.$\overline{142857}$ _____

Directions: For Numbers 9 through 14, write whether each statement is true or false.

9. 0 is an irrational number. _____

10. $-13\frac{4}{7}$ is a rational number. _____

11. Some irrational numbers are not real. _____

12. Every terminating decimal is a rational number. _____

13. Every real number is either rational or irrational. _____

14. Some repeating decimals are irrational. _____

Equivalent Forms of Rational Numbers

Fractions, decimals, and percents are various ways of representing rational numbers and expressing part of a whole.

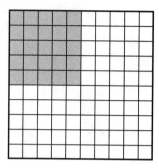

For example, the grid above shows 25 of its 100 units shaded. As a fraction, this is written $\frac{25}{100}$. As a decimal, it is written 0.25. As a percent, it is written 25%. $\frac{25}{100}$, 0.25, and 25% are equivalent expressions. They each represent 25 parts of the whole.

The relationship between fractions, decimals, and percents allows us to convert a fraction to a decimal and a percent.

Converting a fraction to a decimal

To convert a fraction to a decimal, divide the numerator by the denominator until the decimal terminates or repeats a digit or block of digits. (Use a bar, ‾, to show the repeating digit or block of digits.)

Examples

Write $\frac{3}{8}$ as a decimal.

```
    0.375
8)3.000
  − 2 4↓
      60
    − 56↓
        40
      − 40
          0
```

Therefore, $\frac{3}{8} = 0.375$.

Write $\frac{1}{6}$ as a decimal.

```
    0.166
6)1.000
  − 6↓
     40
   − 36↓
       40
     − 36
         4   (repeating)
```

Therefore, $\frac{1}{6} = 0.1\overline{6}$.

Converting a fraction to a percent

To convert a fraction to a percent, first divide the numerator by the denominator to find the decimal form. Next, move the decimal point two places to the right. Finally, write the percent sign, %.

Examples

Write $\frac{3}{8}$ as a percent.

The decimal form of $\frac{3}{8}$ is 0.375,

so the percent is 37.5%.

Therefore, $\frac{3}{8}$ = 37.5%.

Write $\frac{1}{6}$ as a percent.

The decimal form of $\frac{1}{6}$ is $0.1\overline{6}$,

so the percent is $16.\overline{6}\%$.

Therefore, $\frac{1}{6} = 16.\overline{6}\%$.

Practice

Directions: For Numbers 1 through 3, convert to the given forms.

1. Convert $\frac{3}{4}$ to a: decimal _____ percent _____

2. Convert $\frac{2}{9}$ to a: decimal _____ percent _____

3. Convert $\frac{5}{8}$ to a: decimal _____ percent _____

4. Write the equivalent forms (decimal, percent, and fraction) of any rational number.

_____

5. How is $\frac{25}{30}$ written as a decimal?

   A. 1.2
   B. $0.8\overline{3}$
   C. 0.65
   D. $0.5\overline{6}$

6. How is $\frac{17}{20}$ written as a percent?

   A. 70%
   B. 78%
   C. 85%
   D. 92%

Absolute Value

The **absolute value** of a number a, $|a|$, is the distance a is from zero on a number line. Since distances are always regarded as positive, the absolute value of every number will be either positive or 0.

Example

What are the absolute values of 7 and −7?

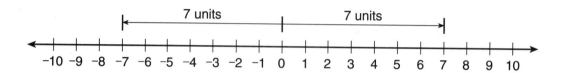

Notice on the number line that both −7 and 7 are 7 units from zero. Therefore, $|7| = 7$ and $|-7| = 7$.

Negative signs on the outside of absolute value signs mean you take the opposite of the absolute value.

Example

What is $-|-50|$? (What is the opposite of the absolute value of −50?)

$$-|-50| = -(50) = -50$$

Practice

Directions: For Numbers 1 through 8, find the absolute value.

1. $|2| = $ _____

2. $|-26| = $ _____

3. $|-\frac{5}{7}| = $ _____

4. $-|4.56| = ?$

   A. −4.56
   B. −4
   C. 4
   D. 4.56

5. $-|-4.25| = $ _____

6. $|0.254| = $ _____

7. $-|-3\frac{2}{5}| = $ _____

8. $|\pi| = ?$

   A. $-\pi$
   B. π
   C. 3
   D. There is no absolute value for π.

Exponents

An **exponent** shows how many times a **base number** occurs as a factor. This is sometimes referred to as **repeated multiplication**.

Example

Evaluate: 2^3

The exponent (^{3}) shows that the base number (2) occurs as a factor 3 times.

$$\overset{\textbf{exponent}}{\underset{\textbf{base number}}{2^3 = 2 \bullet 2 \bullet 2 = 8}}$$

Therefore, $2^3 = 8$.

When working with exponents, remember the following rules:

1. **Any base number (except zero) with zero as the exponent equals 1.**

   $10^0 = 1$ $5^0 = 1$ $25{,}000{,}000^0 = 1$

2. **Any base number with 1 as the exponent equals the same number.**

   $10^1 = 10$ $5^1 = 5$ $25{,}000{,}000^1 = 25{,}000{,}000$

A **negative exponent** indicates a fraction. This can be shown by looking at the pattern that develops in the following table.

Exponent	2^3	2^2	2^1	2^0	2^{-1}	2^{-2}	2^{-3}
Means	$2 \bullet 2 \bullet 2$	$2 \bullet 2$	2	1	$\frac{1}{2}$	$\frac{1}{2} \bullet \frac{1}{2}$	$\frac{1}{2} \bullet \frac{1}{2} \bullet \frac{1}{2}$
Equals	8	4	2	1	$\frac{1}{2}$	$\frac{1}{4}$	$\frac{1}{8}$

As you look from left to right, notice that each new number is found by dividing the previous number by 2. This is sometimes referred to as **repeated division**.

 TIP: Exponents are called **powers** when you read them. 6^4 is read "six to the fourth power." Likewise, 5^{-4} is read "five to the negative fourth power." An exponent of 2 can be read as "second power" or "squared," and an exponent of 3 can be read as "third power" or "cubed."

If a base number has a negative exponent, write the base number as its **reciprocal** (flip it over in fraction form) and change the exponent to its opposite.

Example

Evaluate: 4^{-5}

Since the exponent is a negative number ($^{-5}$), write the base number (4) as its reciprocal $\left(\frac{1}{4}\right)$ and change $^{-5}$ to ^{5}.

$$4^{-5} = \left(\frac{1}{4}\right)^5 = \frac{1}{4} \cdot \frac{1}{4} \cdot \frac{1}{4} \cdot \frac{1}{4} \cdot \frac{1}{4} = \frac{1}{1,024}$$

Therefore, $4^{-5} = \frac{1}{1,024}$.

Practice

Directions: For Numbers 1 through 6, write the meaning of the exponent using repeated multiplication and then evaluate.

1. 9^3: _____ = _____

2. π^0: _____ = _____

3. $(-8)^2$: _____ = _____

4. 6^{-4}: _____ = _____

5. 12^1: _____ = _____

6. $(-4)^{-3}$: _____ = _____

Directions: For Numbers 7 through 14, write each number using an exponent other than 1.

7. $49 =$ _____

8. $-\frac{1}{27} =$ _____

9. $-8 =$ _____

10. $\frac{36}{121} =$ _____

11. $\frac{1}{25} =$ _____

12. $-125 =$ _____

13. $81 =$ _____

14. $\frac{8}{27} =$ _____

Scientific Notation

Scientific notation is used to represent very large or very small numbers. In scientific notation, a large or small number is written as a number greater than or equal to 1 and less than 10 multiplied by a power of 10.

Example

The following numbers are written first in standard form and then in scientific notation.

$$123,000 = 1.23 \cdot 10^5$$
$$0.0000003402 = 3.402 \cdot 10^{-7}$$

Changing from standard form to scientific notation

The following examples show the steps used to change any number from standard form to scientific notation.

Example

Write 3,945,600 in scientific notation.

Step 1: **Move the decimal point to the *left* until you have a number greater than or equal to 1 and less than 10.**

3.945600.

3.945600

Step 2: **Count the number of places you moved the decimal point to the *left*.**

In this example, the decimal point was moved **6** places to the left.

Step 3: **Use that number as an exponent to show the power of 10.**

10^6

Step 4: **Write an expression with the decimal** (from Step 1) **times the power of 10** (from Step 3).

$3.9456 \cdot 10^6$

Therefore, $3,945,600 = 3.9456 \cdot 10^6$.

Example

Write 0.0000451 in scientific notation.

Step 1: Move the decimal point to the *right* until you have a number greater than or equal to 1 and less than 10.

0.00004.51

4.51

Step 2: Count the number of places you moved the decimal point to the *right*.

In this example, the decimal point was moved **5** places to the right.

Step 3: Use that number as a negative exponent to show the power of 10.

10^{-5}

Step 4: Write an expression with the decimal (from Step 1) times the power of 10 (from Step 3).

$4.51 \cdot 10^{-5}$

Therefore, $0.0000451 = 4.51 \cdot 10^{-5}$.

This table shows the values of the powers of ten.

Powers of 10	
Positive	**Negative**
$10^{1} = 10$	$10^{-1} = 0.1$
$10^{2} = 100$	$10^{-2} = 0.01$
$10^{3} = 1,000$	$10^{-3} = 0.001$
$10^{4} = 10,000$	$10^{-4} = 0.0001$
$10^{5} = 100,000$	$10^{-5} = 0.00001$
and so on . . .	and so on . . .

Changing from scientific notation to standard form

To change a number written in scientific notation with a positive power of 10 to standard form, move the decimal point to the **right**. The exponent tells you the number of places to move the decimal point. Remember to add zeros as placeholders when necessary.

Example

$$6.173 \cdot 10^7 = 6.1730000. = 61,730,000$$

To change a number written in scientific notation with a negative power of 10 to standard form, move the decimal point to the **left**. The exponent tells you the number of places to move the decimal point. Remember to add zeros as placeholders when necessary.

Example

$$9.232 \cdot 10^{-4} = 0.0009.232 = 0.0009232$$

Practice

Directions: For Numbers 1 through 8, write the number in scientific notation.

1. $0.29025 =$ _____

2. $5,033 =$ _____

3. $174,355 =$ _____

4. $0.0002012 =$ _____

5. $80,034,000 =$ _____

6. $0.00000821 =$ _____

7. $600,000,000 =$ _____

8. $0.01023 =$ _____

Directions: For Numbers 9 through 16, write the number in standard form.

9. $2.81168 \cdot 10^{-3} =$ _____

13. $6.524 \cdot 10^5 =$ _____

10. $8.7 \cdot 10^8 =$ _____

14. $5.00961 \cdot 10^{-4} =$ _____

11. $4.002 \cdot 10^6 =$ _____

15. $8.34 \cdot 10^{-2} =$ _____

12. $9.2008 \cdot 10^{-7} =$ _____

16. $1 \cdot 10^9 =$ _____

Directions: For Numbers 17 through 24, use $<$, $>$, or $=$ to compare.

17. $8.453 \cdot 10^4$ _____ $845{,}300$

21. 2 million _____ $2 \cdot 10^7$

18. 0.000032 _____ $3.2 \cdot 10^{-5}$

22. $6.34 \cdot 10^{-7}$ _____ 0.0000000634

19. 4 thousandths _____ $4 \cdot 10^{-4}$

23. $5.32 \cdot 10^3$ _____ $5{,}320$

20. $2.187 \cdot 10^3$ _____ 3^7

24. fifty thousand _____ $5 \cdot 10^5$

Square Roots

Square roots are indicated by the use of the radical sign ($\sqrt{}$). To find the square root of a number, find the number that when multiplied by itself is equal to the number under the radical sign (radicand).

Examples

Evaluate: $\sqrt{16}$

$16 = 4 \bullet 4$

$16 = (-4) \bullet (-4)$

Therefore, $\sqrt{16} = \pm 4$.

Evaluate: $\sqrt{25}$

$25 = 5 \bullet 5$

$25 = (-5) \bullet (-5)$

Therefore, $\sqrt{25} = \pm 5$.

Numbers such as 1, 4, 9, 16, and 25 are called **perfect squares** because their square roots are rational numbers. Notice that there are two square roots for each perfect square. The **principal** (positive) square root is all that is required in most situations.

Estimating square roots of nonperfect squares

Numbers such as 2, 3, and 5 are not perfect squares. The square roots of numbers that are not perfect squares are irrational numbers. You can estimate the square root of a nonperfect square by determining between which two rational numbers the root lies.

Example

Evaluate: $\sqrt{29}$

Since 29 is not a perfect square, determine between which two perfect squares 29 lies. 29 lies between the perfect squares 25 and 36.

Evaluate the square roots of 25 and 36: 5 and 6.

Since 29 lies between 25 and 36, $\sqrt{29}$ lies between 5 and 6. (A calculator shows that $\sqrt{29} = 5.385164807\ldots$)

TIP: When evaluating the square root of a fraction, evaluate the square root of the numerator and the square root of the denominator.

$$\sqrt{\frac{36}{169}} = \frac{\sqrt{36}}{\sqrt{169}} = \frac{6}{13}$$

Practice

Directions: For Numbers 1 through 10, evaluate the square root.

1. $\sqrt{49} =$ _____

2. $\sqrt{4} =$ _____

3. $\sqrt{100} =$ _____

4. $\sqrt{225} =$ _____

5. $\sqrt{81} =$ _____

6. $\sqrt{144} =$ _____

7. $\sqrt{64} =$ _____

8. $\sqrt{\frac{4}{9}} =$ _____

9. $\sqrt{\frac{1}{121}} =$ _____

10. $\sqrt{\frac{16}{25}} =$ _____

Directions: For Numbers 11 through 13, determine between which two rational numbers the square root lies. Explain.

11. $\sqrt{75}$:

12. $\sqrt{46}$:

13. $\sqrt{107}$:

14. Evaluate: $\sqrt{289}$

  A. 15
  B. 16
  C. 17
  D. 18

15. Between which two rational numbers does $\sqrt{503}$ lie?

  A. 19 and 20
  B. 20 and 21
  C. 21 and 22
  D. 22 and 23

Multiples and Factors

Multiples of a number are the products that result from multiplying the number by the whole numbers (0, 1, 2, 3, 4, and so on).

Example

The multiples of 5 are 0, 5, 10, 15, 20, . . .

A number that is a multiple of two or more numbers is a **common multiple**. (Zero is not considered a common multiple.)

Example

The multiples of 2 are 0, 2, 4, 6, 8, **10**, 12, 14, 16, 18, **20**, . . .

The multiples of 5 are 0, 5, **10**, 15, **20**, 25, . . .

The numbers 10 and 20 are multiples of both 2 and 5. Therefore, 10 and 20 are **common multiples** of 2 and 5.

The smallest of the common multiples is called the **least common multiple (LCM)**. The least common multiple of 2 and 5 is **10**.

Factors of a number divide that number evenly (no remainder).

Examples

What numbers divide 16 evenly?

$16 \div \mathbf{1} = 16$

$16 \div \mathbf{2} = 8$

$16 \div \mathbf{4} = 4$

$16 \div \mathbf{8} = 2$

$16 \div \mathbf{16} = 1$

The factors of 16 are 1, 2, 4, 8, and 16.

What numbers divide 20 evenly?

$20 \div \mathbf{1} = 20$

$20 \div \mathbf{2} = 10$

$20 \div \mathbf{4} = 5$

$20 \div \mathbf{5} = 4$

$20 \div \mathbf{10} = 2$

$20 \div \mathbf{20} = 1$

The factors of 20 are 1, 2, 4, 5, 10, and 20.

Common factors of 16 and 20 are 1, 2, and 4. Since 4 is the largest of the common factors, it is the **greatest common factor (GCF)** of 16 and 20.

Practice

Directions: For Numbers 1 through 6, fill in the missing multiples.

1. Multiples of 4: 0, _____, 8, _____, 16, 20, 24, . . .

2. Multiples of 6: 0, 6, 12, 18, _____, _____, . . .

3. Multiples of 8: 0, 8, 16, _____, _____, 40, . . .

4. Multiples of 9: 0, 9, 18, _____, 36, _____, . . .

5. Multiples of 12: 0, 12, _____, _____, . . .

6. Multiples of 15: 0, 15, _____, _____, . . .

7. What is the **least common multiple** of 6 and 15? _____

8. What is the **least common multiple** of 8 and 9? _____

Directions: For Numbers 9 through 12, list all the factors.

9. Factors of 7: _____

10. Factors of 14: _____

11. Factors of 10: _____

12. Factors of 21: _____

13. What is the **greatest common factor** of 10 and 14? _____

14. What is the **greatest common factor** of 7 and 21? _____

Prime and Composite Numbers

Prime numbers have only two factors: 1 and the number. **Composite numbers** have at least three factors. 0 and 1 are neither prime nor composite numbers.

Examples

2, 3, and 5 have only two factors. They are prime numbers.

Factors of 2: 1 and 2   3: 1 and 3   5: 1 and 5

4 has three factors. It is a composite number.

Factors of 4: 1, 2, and 4

Practice

1. Is 6 a prime number or a composite number? _____

2. Is 7 a prime number or a composite number? _____

3. Is 9 a prime number or a composite number? _____

4. List all the prime numbers **between** 10 and 20.

   _____

5. List all the composite numbers **between** 10 and 20.

   _____

6. Which is a prime number?

   A. 23
   B. 33
   C. 49
   D. 51

7. Which is a composite number?

   A. 29
   B. 43
   C. 73
   D. 93

Prime Factorization

Prime factorization is a way of expressing a composite number as a product of prime numbers. **Factor trees** help you determine the prime factorization of composite numbers.

 Example

What is the prime factorization of 24?

Write the number 24. Put a *prime* factor under the left branch and circle it. Put the *nonprime* factor under the right branch. Repeat the process until you have circled two prime numbers at the bottom of the tree.

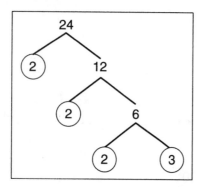

The prime factorization of 24 is 2 • 2 • 2 • 3 or 2^3 • 3.

 **Practice**

1. Draw a factor tree for 45.

The prime factorization of 45 is _____ .

2. Draw a factor tree for 120.

The prime factorization of 120 is _____ .

3. Draw a factor tree for 1,260.

The prime factorization of 1,260 is _____ .

Test Your Skills

1. What is the value of 3^{-3}?

   A. -27

   B. -9

   C. $\frac{1}{9}$

   D. $\frac{1}{27}$

2. What is the greatest common factor of 18 and 30?

   A. 6
   B. 9
   C. 12
   D. 15

3. How is $\frac{4}{15}$ written as a decimal?

   A. $0.1\overline{8}$
   B. $0.2\overline{6}$
   C. 0.375
   D. 0.6

4. Which is a prime number?

   A. 21
   B. 37
   C. 45
   D. 57

5. What is the value of $(-2)^4$?

   A. -16
   B. -8
   C. 8
   D. 16

6. What is $|-8.34|$?

   A. -8.34
   B. -8
   C. 8
   D. 8.34

7. How is $\frac{7}{8}$ written as a percent?

   A. 78%
   B. 85%
   C. 87.5%
   D. 92.5%

8. How is $2.35 \cdot 10^4$ written in standard form?

   A.   0.0002350
   B.   235
   C.   23,500
   D. 235,000

9. What is another way of writing $10 \cdot 10 \cdot 10 \cdot 10 \cdot 10$?

   A. 5^{10}
   B. 10^5
   C. 5^{-10}
   D. 10^{-5}

10. Between which two rational numbers does $\sqrt{85}$ lie?

    A. 9 and 10
    B. 8 and 9
    C. 7 and 8
    D. 6 and 7

11. What is the least common multiple of 8 and 10?

    A. 20
    B. 40
    C. 60
    D. 80

12. Which statement is **false**?

    A. $4.3 \cdot 10^2 = 430$
    B. $0.000439 = 4.39 \cdot 10^{-4}$
    C. $2.51 \cdot 10^4 < 8.32 \cdot 10^{-5}$
    D. $-5.4 \cdot 10^4 < -5.4 \cdot 10^{-3}$

13. What is another way of writing 64?

    A. 2^6
    B. $-|-64|$
    C. $6.4 \cdot 10^2$
    D. $4 \cdot 4 \cdot 4 \cdot 4$

14. What is the prime factorization of 1,350?

    A. $2 \cdot 5^4$
    B. $2 \cdot 3^4 \cdot 5$
    C. $2 \cdot 3^3 \cdot 5^2$
    D. $2^2 \cdot 3^2 \cdot 5^2$

15. How is 0.000054 written in scientific notation?

    A. $54 \cdot 10^{-6}$
    B. $54 \cdot 10^{-5}$
    C. $5.4 \cdot 10^{-6}$
    D. $5.4 \cdot 10^{-5}$

Lesson 2: Operations

This lesson will review the four operations of addition, subtraction, multiplication, and division of integers, fractions, and decimals. It will also review laws of exponents and order of operations.

Integers

The integers are the counting numbers (1, 2, 3, and so on), their opposites (−1, −2, −3, and so on), and zero.

Addition and subtraction

Here are a few things to remember when adding or subtracting integers.

- The sum of two positive integers is positive.

  $47 + 22 = 69$

  $1,246 + 4,238 = 5,484$

- The sum of two negative integers is negative.

  $-17 + (-22) = -39$

  $-925 + (-2,381) = -3,306$

- The sum of one positive and one negative integer will have the sign of the number with the greater absolute value.

  $-11 + 6 = -5$ $(|-11| > |6|)$

  $13 + (-9) = 4$ $(|13| > |-9|)$

- The difference of two integers can be found by adding the opposite.

  $-8 - (-4) = -8 + 4$ $9 - 5 = 9 + (-5)$

           $= -4$ $= 4$

Multiplication and division

Here are a few things to remember when multiplying or dividing integers.

- The product or quotient of two positive integers is positive.

    $7 \cdot 7 = 49$

    $\frac{16}{4} = 4$

- The product or quotient of two negative integers is positive.

    $(-4)(-5) = 20$

    $\frac{-14}{-2} = 7$

- The product or quotient of one positive and one negative integer is negative.

    $3(-4) = -12$

    $\frac{30}{-6} = -5$

Practice

Directions: For Numbers 1 through 14, find the sum, difference, product, or quotient.

1. $19 \cdot (-8) =$ _____

2. $41 + (-8) =$ _____

3. $1{,}024 \div (-32) =$ _____

4. $-22 + (-46) =$ _____

5. $-36 - 36 =$ _____

6. $(8)(-10) =$ _____

7. $159 - (-30) =$ _____

8. $-36 - (-36) =$ _____

9. $-63 \div 3 =$ _____

10. $-62 + 11 =$ _____

11. $106 - (-53) =$ _____

12. $-15 \div (-15) =$ _____

13. $-254 \cdot 28 =$ _____

14. $-34 + 34 =$ _____

Fractions

There are times when fractions need to be rewritten as equivalent fractions or written as improper fractions before you can compute with them.

Addition and subtraction

Common denominators are needed before adding or subtracting fractions.

Example

Add: $\frac{5}{12} + \frac{7}{10}$

Step 1: **Check to see if the fractions have a common denominator. If they do, go on to Step 2; if not, find the least common denominator (LCD), which is the LCM of the denominators. Then rewrite the fractions with the LCD.**

The denominators are 12 and 10, which are not common; therefore, find the LCD. To find the LCD, write the multiples of each.

12: 12, 24, 36, 48, **60**, 72, 84, . . .

10: 10, 20, 30, 40, 50, **60**, . . .

Another way of finding the LCD is by using the prime factorizations of the denominators. Write the prime factorizations of each denominator.

$12 = 2^2 \cdot 3$

$10 = 2 \cdot 5$

Next, multiply all the different prime factors (2, 3, and 5), with each raised to its highest power (^{2}, ^{1}, and ^{1}, respectively). This product is the LCD.

LCD: $2^2 \cdot 3 \cdot 5 = 60$

Rewrite the fractions with 60 as the denominator. Multiply both the numerator and denominator of each fraction by the factor necessary to make the original denominator equal the LCD.

$$\frac{5 \cdot 5}{12 \cdot 5} = \frac{25}{60} \qquad\qquad \frac{7 \cdot 6}{10 \cdot 6} = \frac{42}{60}$$

Step 2: **Add (or subtract) the numerators, keeping the denominator the same. Write the sum (or difference) in lowest terms.**

$$\frac{25}{60} + \frac{42}{60} = \frac{67}{60} = 1\frac{7}{60}$$

Therefore, $\frac{5}{12} + \frac{7}{10} = 1\frac{7}{60}$.

Example

Subtract: $-\frac{23}{40} - \frac{13}{210}$

Find the LCD and rewrite the fractions.

40: $2^3 \cdot 5$

210: $2 \cdot 3 \cdot 5 \cdot 7$

LCD: $2^3 \cdot 3 \cdot 5 \cdot 7 = 840$

$$-\frac{23 \cdot 21}{40 \cdot 21} = -\frac{483}{840} \qquad\qquad \frac{13 \cdot 4}{210 \cdot 4} = \frac{52}{840}$$

Subtract the numerators, keep the denominators the same, and write the difference in lowest terms.

$$-\frac{483}{840} - \frac{52}{840} = -\frac{535}{840} = -\frac{107}{168}$$

Therefore, $-\frac{23}{40} - \frac{13}{210} = -\frac{107}{168}$.

When adding or subtracting mixed numbers, first write the mixed numbers as improper fractions, then follow the steps for adding or subtracting fractions.

Example

Add: $-3\frac{5}{8} + 4\frac{7}{15}$

Write $-3\frac{5}{8}$ and $4\frac{7}{15}$ as improper fractions.

$$-3\frac{5}{8} = \frac{-(8 \cdot 3 + 5)}{8} = -\frac{29}{8} \qquad\qquad 4\frac{7}{15} = \frac{15 \cdot 4 + 7}{15} = \frac{67}{15}$$

Follow the steps for adding fractions.

$$-\frac{29}{8} + \frac{67}{15} = -\frac{435}{120} + \frac{536}{120} = \frac{101}{120}$$

$8 \times 15 = 120$

Therefore, $-3\frac{5}{8} + 4\frac{7}{15} = \frac{101}{120}$.

Practice

Directions: For Numbers 1 through 8, find the sum or difference.

1. $\frac{4}{15} + \frac{7}{15} =$ _____

2. $\frac{13}{18} - \frac{5}{18} =$ _____

3. $8\frac{3}{14} - 4\frac{1}{28} =$ _____

4. $\frac{22}{35} + \frac{16}{21} =$ _____

5. $-4\frac{3}{8} + 7\frac{11}{12} =$ _____

6. $\frac{14}{25} - \frac{9}{10} =$ _____

7. $\frac{17}{27} + \left(-\frac{21}{45}\right) =$ _____

8. $-3\frac{13}{24} + \left(-1\frac{11}{15}\right) =$ _____

9. Add: $\frac{15}{28} + \frac{31}{42}$

   A. $\frac{23}{35}$

   B. $\frac{19}{21}$

   C. $1\frac{23}{84}$

   D. $1\frac{11}{42}$

10. Subtract: $-3\frac{4}{21} - 7\frac{5}{6}$

   A. $-12\frac{11}{21}$

   B. $-11\frac{1}{42}$

   C. $-10\frac{5}{21}$

   D. $-10\frac{1}{6}$

Multiplication

Common denominators are not needed when multiplying fractions. To multiply fractions, multiply the numerators, multiply the denominators, and then write the product in lowest terms.

Example

Multiply: $\frac{12}{25} \cdot \frac{10}{27}$

Multiply the numerators (12 and 10), multiply the denominators (25 and 27), and then write the product in lowest terms.

$$\frac{12}{25} \cdot \frac{10}{27} = \frac{12 \cdot 10}{25 \cdot 27} = \frac{120}{675} \div \frac{15}{15} = \frac{8}{45}$$

Therefore, $\frac{12}{25} \cdot \frac{10}{27} = \frac{8}{45}$.

If you notice that a numerator and a denominator from different fractions have a common factor, divide both the numerator and denominator by that common factor before multiplying. Remember to check the product to be sure it is in lowest terms.

Example

Multiply: $\frac{12}{25} \cdot \frac{10}{27}$

Notice that 12 and 27 have a common factor of 3, and 10 and 25 have a common factor of 5. Divide these factors before multiplying the numerators and denominators.

$$\overset{4}{\underset{5}{\cancel{\frac{12}{25}}}} \cdot \overset{2}{\underset{9}{\cancel{\frac{10}{27}}}} = \frac{8}{45}$$

Therefore, $\frac{12}{25} \cdot \frac{10}{27} = \frac{8}{45}$.

When multiplying mixed numbers or integers, first write the mixed numbers as improper fractions and the integers as fractions (by writing them over 1), then follow the steps for multiplying fractions.

Division

Dividing by a fraction is the same as multiplying by the reciprocal of the fraction. Think of a reciprocal as a fraction flipped upside down. For example, the reciprocal of $\frac{3}{10}$ is $\frac{10}{3}$. To divide fractions, change division to multiplication and the **divisor** (the fraction you're dividing by) to its reciprocal. Remember **not** to change the **dividend** (the fraction that is being divided). Then follow the procedure for multiplying fractions.

Example

Divide: $\frac{18}{35} \div \frac{9}{14}$

Change $\div$ to $\bullet$ and $\frac{9}{14}$ to $\frac{14}{9}$, then multiply.

$$\frac{18}{35} \div \frac{9}{14} = \frac{\overset{2}{\cancel{18}}}{\underset{5}{\cancel{35}}} \bullet \frac{\overset{2}{\cancel{14}}}{\underset{1}{\cancel{9}}} = \frac{4}{5}$$

Therefore, $\frac{18}{35} \div \frac{9}{14} = \frac{4}{5}$.

As with multiplication, change mixed numbers to improper fractions and integers to fractions (by writing them over 1) before dividing the fractions.

Practice

Directions: For Numbers 1 through 8, find the product or quotient.

1. $\frac{9}{35} \bullet \frac{28}{45} =$ _____

2. $5\frac{1}{8} \div \frac{3}{4} =$ _____

3. $6\frac{2}{3} \bullet \left(-3\frac{3}{4}\right) =$ _____

4. $-10\frac{3}{5} \div \left(-3\frac{1}{3}\right) =$ _____

5. $-\frac{7}{10} \div \frac{2}{5} =$ _____

6. $\frac{8}{11} \div 4 =$ _____

7. $3 \bullet \left(-\frac{6}{7}\right) =$ _____

8. $\frac{21}{22} \bullet \left(-5\frac{2}{7}\right) =$ _____

Decimals

The placement of the decimal point in a sum, difference, product, or quotient is very important.

Addition and subtraction

To add or subtract decimals, line up the decimal points. Then add or subtract as you would whole numbers. Finally, move the decimal point straight down into the sum or difference. You may need to add zeros as placeholders when lining up the decimal points.

Example

Subtract: $245.873 - 45.78$

Line up the decimal points and add a zero as a placeholder in 45.78. Then subtract and move the decimal point straight down into the difference.

$$
\begin{array}{r}
^{7}{}_{1} \\
245.\overset{}{8}73 \\
-\quad 45.780 \\
\hline
200.093
\end{array}
$$

Therefore, $245.873 - 45.78 = 200.093$.

Practice

Directions: For Numbers 1 through 10, find the sum or difference.

1. $893.23 + 78.961 =$ _____

2. $1,892 - 8.543 =$ _____

3. $0.0234 + 6.0982 =$ _____

4. $-8,916.23 - 23.8942 =$ _____

5. $32.498 + 7.105 =$ _____

6. $325.65002 - 98.5672 =$ _____

7. $-398.312 + 3,498.32 =$ _____

8. $-54.34 + (-873.87) =$ _____

9. $34 - (-135.982) =$ _____

10. $-127.48 - 49.532 =$ _____

Multiplication

To multiply decimals, multiply as if they were whole numbers. Then add the number of digits to the right of the decimal point in each factor. Finally, move the decimal point that many places to the left in the product.

Example

Multiply: 245.76 • 34.5

Multiply. Since there are a total of three digits to the right of the decimal point in the factors, move the decimal point three places to the left in the product.

$$
\begin{array}{r}
245.76 \\
\times\quad 34.5 \\
\hline
122880 \\
983040 \\
7372800 \\
\hline
8{,}478{,}720 \\
\end{array}
$$

Therefore, 245.76 • 34.5 = 8,478.72.

Division

If the divisor is not a whole number, move the decimal point to the right to make it a whole number. Move the decimal point in the dividend to the right the same number of places. Then divide as if they were whole numbers. Finally, move the decimal point straight up from its new location into the quotient.

Example

Divide: 50.54 ÷ 1.4

Move the decimal point one place to the right in both the divisor and the dividend to make the divisor a whole number. Then divide and move the decimal point straight up into the quotient.

$$
\begin{array}{r}
3\,6.1 \\
1.4.\overline{)50.5.4} \\
-\,42 \\
\hline
8\,5 \\
-\,8\,4 \\
\hline
1\,4 \\
-\,1\,4 \\
\hline
0 \\
\end{array}
$$

Therefore, 50.54 ÷ 1.4 = 36.1.

Practice

Directions: For Numbers 1 through 8, find the product or quotient.

1. $45.3 \cdot 2.34 =$ _____

2. $26{,}992 \div 2.8 =$ _____

3. $4.41 \div 9 =$ _____

4. $37.98 \div 0.9 =$ _____

5. $2.98 \cdot 0.023 =$ _____

6. $64.2 \cdot 3.4 =$ _____

7. $480 \cdot 9.402 =$ _____

8. $739.31 \div 14.3 =$ _____

9. Divide: $3{,}485 \div 0.17$

    A. 20,500

    B. 2,050

    C.   205

    D.   20.5

10. Multiply: $3.409 \cdot 0.15$

    A. 511.35

    B. 51.135

    C.   5.1135

    D.   0.51135

Laws of Exponents

There are certain laws to follow when multiplying or dividing the same base raised to a power or when simplifying a power of a power.

Multiplication

When multiplying powers with the same base number, add the exponents and keep the base number the same.

Example

Multiply: $2^3 \cdot 2^7$

$$2^3 \cdot 2^7 = (2 \cdot 2 \cdot 2) \cdot (2 \cdot 2 \cdot 2 \cdot 2 \cdot 2 \cdot 2 \cdot 2)$$

$$= 2^{3+7} = 2^{10} = 1{,}024$$

Therefore, $2^3 \cdot 2^7 = 2^{10}$ or $1{,}024$.

Division

When dividing powers with the same base number, subtract the exponent in the denominator from the exponent in the numerator and keep the base number the same.

Example

Divide: $\frac{3^8}{3^5}$

$$\frac{3^8}{3^5} = \frac{\overset{1}{\cancel{3}} \cdot \overset{1}{\cancel{3}} \cdot \overset{1}{\cancel{3}} \cdot \overset{1}{\cancel{3}} \cdot \overset{1}{\cancel{3}} \cdot 3 \cdot 3 \cdot 3}{\underset{1}{\cancel{3}} \cdot \underset{1}{\cancel{3}} \cdot \underset{1}{\cancel{3}} \cdot \underset{1}{\cancel{3}} \cdot \underset{1}{\cancel{3}}}$$

$$= 3^{8-5} = 3^3 = 27$$

Therefore, $\frac{3^8}{3^5} = 3^3$ or 27.

Recall the meaning of a negative exponent from Lesson 1.

Example

Divide: $\frac{2^2}{2^4}$

$$\frac{2^2}{2^4} = \frac{\overset{1}{\cancel{2}} \cdot \overset{1}{\cancel{2}}}{\underset{1}{\cancel{2}} \cdot \underset{1}{\cancel{2}} \cdot 2 \cdot 2}$$

$$= 2^{2-4} = 2^{-2} = \left(\frac{1}{2}\right)^2 = \frac{1}{4}$$

Therefore, $\frac{2^2}{2^4} = 2^{-2}$, $\left(\frac{1}{2}\right)^2$, or $\frac{1}{4}$.

Power of a power

When simplifying a power of a power, multiply the exponents and keep the base number the same.

Example

Simplify: $(5^3)^2$

$$(5^3)^2 = 5^{3 \cdot 2} = 5^6 = 15{,}625$$

Therefore, $(5^3)^2 = 5^6$ or $15{,}625$.

Practice

Directions: For Numbers 1 through 8, multiply, divide, or simplify. Write your answer both using exponents and as a rational number.

1. $(8^2)^2 = $ _____ or _____

2. $3^{-2} \cdot 3^4 = $ _____ or _____

3. $(2^{-3})^2 = $ _____ or _____

4. $(-6)^4 \cdot (-6) = $ _____ or _____

5. $9^2 \cdot 9^4 = $ _____ or _____

6. $\frac{10^5}{10^8} = $ _____ or _____

7. $\frac{(-4)^6}{(-4)^3} = $ _____ or _____

8. $(3^2)^{-3} = $ _____ or _____

The laws of exponents play a role when you are reducing, multiplying, or dividing fractions. When reducing a fraction, find the prime factorization of the numerator and denominator. Then use the law of exponents for division to simplify the common bases. When multiplying fractions, write the prime factorizations of each numerator and denominator. Then use the law of exponents for division to simplify the common bases of **any** numerator and denominator. Finally, use the law of exponents for multiplication to multiply the fractions. When dividing fractions, rewrite division as multiplication. Then use the laws of exponents to simplify and multiply.

Example

Simplify: $\dfrac{24}{90}$

$$\frac{24}{90} = \frac{\overset{2}{2^{\cancel{3}}} \cdot \overset{1}{\cancel{3}}}{\underset{1}{\cancel{2}} \cdot 3\underset{1}{^{\cancel{2}}} \cdot 5} = \frac{2^2}{3 \cdot 5} = \frac{4}{15}$$

Therefore, $\dfrac{24}{90} = \dfrac{4}{15}$.

Example

Multiply: $\dfrac{40}{63} \cdot \dfrac{75}{196}$

$$\frac{40}{63} \cdot \frac{75}{196} = \frac{2^{\cancel{3}} \cdot 5}{3\underset{1}{^{\cancel{2}}} \cdot 7} \cdot \frac{\overset{1}{\cancel{3}} \cdot 5^2}{\underset{1}{2^{\cancel{2}}} \cdot 7^2} = \frac{2 \cdot 5^3}{3 \cdot 7^3} = \frac{250}{1,029}$$

Therefore, $\dfrac{40}{63} \cdot \dfrac{75}{196} = \dfrac{250}{1,029}$.

Practice

Directions: For Numbers 1 through 4, use the laws of exponents to simplify, multiply, or divide.

1. $\dfrac{21}{140} =$ _____

2. $2\dfrac{4}{5} \div 1\dfrac{3}{7} =$ _____

3. $\dfrac{12}{25} \cdot \dfrac{10}{27} =$ _____

4. $\dfrac{1,925}{3,080} =$ _____

Order of Operations

When solving a problem that involves more than one operation, it is very important to follow the **order of operations** correctly. The following list shows the order in which you need to perform the operations.

1. **Simplify all expressions inside parentheses.**

2. **Simplify all expressions with exponents.**

3. **Perform all multiplication and division in order from left to right.**

4. **Perform all addition and subtraction in order from left to right.**

Example

Simplify: $12 + 36 \div 4 \cdot 3^2$

There are no parentheses, so simplify all expressions with exponents.

$12 + 36 \div 4 \cdot \mathbf{9}$

Perform all multiplication and division in order from left to right.

$12 + \mathbf{9} \cdot 9$

$12 + \mathbf{81}$

Perform all addition and subtraction in order from left to right.

93

Therefore, $12 + 36 \div 4 \cdot 3^2 = 93$.

Practice

Directions: For Numbers 1 through 4, use the order of operations to simplify each expression.

1. $25 - 5 \div 1 + 4.5 - 3$

2. $10 \div 2 - 35 + (9 - 7)$

3. $11 + (27 \div 9)^2 \cdot 4$

4. $\frac{4}{5}\left(\frac{1}{4} + \frac{3}{5}\right) - \left(\frac{2}{5}\right)^2$

Test Your Skills

1. Divide:

$$8\frac{4}{5} \div 2\frac{2}{5}$$

A. $3\frac{2}{3}$

B. $4\frac{2}{5}$

C. $5\frac{1}{3}$

D. 6

2. John had $145.76 in his money jar. He took $17.48 from the jar to buy some school supplies. How much money does John now have in his money jar?

A. $128.28
B. $138.38
C. $153.14
D. $163.24

3. During one day, the value of a stock lost 4 points (−4) in the morning and then gained 7 points (+7) in the afternoon. What was the overall loss or gain of the stock's value for that day?

A. gained 11 points
B. gained 3 points
C. lost 11 points
D. lost 3 points

4. Simplify:

$$(4^3)^2$$

A.   128
B.   1,024
C.   4,096
D. 262,144

5. Trevor read $\frac{1}{3}$ of his library book on Saturday and $\frac{2}{5}$ of it on Sunday. What part of the book did Trevor read on Saturday and Sunday combined?

A. $\frac{3}{8}$

B. $\frac{5}{8}$

C. $\frac{2}{15}$

D. $\frac{11}{15}$

6. Divide:

$$\frac{6^3}{6^8}$$

A. 6^5

B. 6^{-5}

C. (-6^5)

D. $\left(\frac{1}{6}\right)^{-5}$

7. Helga is walking a wilderness trail that is $3\frac{1}{2}$ miles long. She has walked $\frac{3}{4}$ of the trail. How many miles of the trail has Helga walked?

A. $2\frac{1}{8}$

B. $2\frac{3}{8}$

C. $2\frac{5}{8}$

D. $2\frac{7}{8}$

8. What is the product of $\frac{5}{8}$ and 0.65 expressed as a decimal? Convert $\frac{5}{8}$ to a decimal before finding the product.

A. 0.2875
B. 0.3025
C. 0.33875
D. 0.40625

9. How many nickels is $4.85?

A. 89
B. 93
C. 97
D. 101

10. Mr. Castillo wrote the following problem on the board.

Simplify:

$$-2(3 + 9 \bullet 2^2) + (-8) \div \frac{1}{2}$$

Here are four students' solutions.

Rico: −62

Gina: −94

Trudy: −112

Sonny: −172

Which student's solution is correct?

A. Rico
B. Gina
C. Trudy
D. Sonny

11. Uma had a board that was $6\frac{1}{3}$ feet long. She cut the board into two pieces. One of the pieces is 4.3125 feet long. **About** how long is the other piece?

A. 1.8275 feet
B. 2.0208 feet
C. 2.2496 feet
D. 2.5481 feet

Lesson 3: Consumer Mathematics

Consumer mathematics is the branch of mathematics that deals with using math in your everyday life, including the calculation of personal finances.

Percent of Increase or Decrease

The percent of increase or decrease is found by using a **ratio**. A ratio is a comparison of two numbers, usually expressed as a fraction.

Percent of increase

To find the **percent of increase**, use the following ratio.

$$\frac{\text{new amount} - \text{original amount}}{\text{original amount}}$$

Convert the fraction to a decimal, then to a percent.

Example

The price of gas went from $1.62 per gallon to $1.93 per gallon. What is the percent of increase? Round to the nearest percent.

$$\frac{\text{new amount} - \text{original amount}}{\text{original amount}} = \frac{1.93 - 1.62}{1.62}$$

$$= \frac{0.31}{1.62}$$

$$= 0.191358024 \ldots \approx 19\%$$

The price of gas increased by about 19%.

Example

Last year, Herbert's average math score was 82. This year, his average math score is 88. What is the percent of increase? Round to the nearest percent.

$$\frac{\text{new amount} - \text{original amount}}{\text{original amount}} = \frac{88 - 82}{82}$$

$$= \frac{6}{82}$$

$$= 0.07317073 \ldots \approx 7\%$$

Herbert's average math score increased by about 7%.

Percent of decrease

To find the **percent of decrease**, use the following ratio.

original amount − new amount
original amount

Convert the fraction to a decimal, then to a percent.

Example

A shirt that normally sells for $24.99 is on sale for $18.75. What is the percent of decrease? Round to the nearest percent.

$$\frac{\text{original amount} - \text{new amount}}{\text{original amount}} = \frac{24.99 - 18.75}{24.99}$$

$$= \frac{6.24}{24.99}$$

$$= 0.24969987\ldots \approx 25\%$$

The price of the shirt decreased by about 25%.

Practice

Directions: For Numbers 1 through 6, find the percent of increase or decrease. Round to the nearest percent.

1. Ralph's phone bill went from $32.25 to $18.70. _____

2. Sue's weekly allowance went from $10.00 to $12.50. _____

3. The temperature went from 83° to 72°. _____

4. Macy's bill went from $24 to $25.44 when tax was included. _____

5. Vera's time in the 40-yd dash went from 6.4 seconds to 5.6 seconds.

   A. decrease of about 9%
   B. decrease of about 11%
   C. decrease of about 13%
   D. decrease of about 15%

6. Kevin's charge for mowing a lawn went from $10 a month to $16 a month.

   A. increase of 30%
   B. increase of 40%
   C. increase of 50%
   D. increase of 60%

Markup, Commission, Discount, and Profit

Problems involving markup, commission, discount, and profit are solved using equations derived from the percent of increase or decrease ratios.

Markup

Markup is the amount that a retailer (store) adds to the **wholesale price** (the price the retailer pays for an item) to get the **retail price** (the consumer price). To find the amount of markup, multiply the wholesale price by the **markup rate**. Round to the nearest cent.

> **markup = wholesale price • markup rate**

Once the amount of markup is found, you can find the retail price.

> **retail price = wholesale price + markup**

The markup rate is usually expressed as a percent. Convert the markup rate to a decimal before multiplying. To convert a percent to a decimal, remove the percent sign and then move the decimal point two places to the left. For example, 42% = 0.42.

Example

A furniture store pays a wholesale price of $200 for a chair. The store's markup rate is 75%. What is the amount of markup and the retail price of the chair?

First find the amount of markup.

$$\text{markup} = \text{wholesale price} \cdot \text{markup rate}$$
$$= 200 \cdot 0.75$$
$$= \$150$$

Then find the retail price.

$$\text{retail price} = \text{wholesale price} + \text{markup}$$
$$= 200 + 150$$
$$= \$350$$

The chair's amount of markup is $150 and its retail price is $350.

Commission

Commission is the amount of money someone is paid based on a percentage of that person's sales.

To find the amount of commission, multiply the amount of sales by the **commission rate**. Round to the nearest cent.

commission = sales • commission rate

The commission rate is expressed as a percent or a fraction. Convert the commission rate to a decimal before multiplying.

Example

Felipe works at a shoe store in the mall. He earns an 8% commission on his sales. How much commission does Felipe earn for sales of $525?

Find the amount of commission.

$$\text{commission} = \text{sales} \cdot \text{commission rate}$$
$$= 525 \cdot 0.08$$
$$= \$42$$

Felipe earns $42 in commission.

Example

Penelope earns $\frac{1}{10}$ of what she sells as commission. Last week her sales totaled $2,345. How much commission did Penelope earn?

Find the amount of commission.

$$\text{commission} = \text{sales} \cdot \text{commission rate}$$
$$= 2,345 \cdot 0.10 \qquad \left(\tfrac{1}{10} = 0.10\right)$$
$$= \$234.50$$

Penelope earned $234.50 in commission.

Discount

Discount is the amount that an item is reduced from its **retail price** to its **sale price**. To find the amount of discount, multiply the retail price by the **discount rate**. Round to the nearest cent.

discount = retail price • discount rate

Once the amount of discount is found, you can find the sale price.

sale price = retail price − discount

The discount rate may be expressed as a percent or a fraction. Convert the discount rate to a decimal before multiplying.

Example

At a one-day $\frac{1}{4}$-off sale, Nate bought a sweatshirt. If the regular price was \$18.50, what was the sale price?

First find the amount of discount.

discount = retail price • discount rate

$$= 18.50 \bullet 0.25 \qquad \left(\tfrac{1}{4} = 0.25 \right)$$

$$= 4.625 \approx \$4.63$$

Then find the sale price.

sale price = retail price − discount

$$= 18.50 - 4.63$$

$$= \$13.87$$

The sale price of the sweatshirt was \$13.87.

TIP: Taxes are a form of markup, and tips are a form of commission.

Profit

Profit is the amount of money that is left over from the **revenue** (income) after all the **costs** (expenses) are paid.

To find the profit, find the difference between the revenue and the costs.

profit = revenue − costs

Example

A company's revenue for 2002 was $250,000, and its costs were $196,000. How much was the company's profit in 2002?

Find the profit.

$$\text{profit} = \text{revenue} - \text{costs}$$
$$= 250,000 - 196,000$$
$$= 54,000$$

The company's profit was $54,000 in 2002.

The same company had a profit of $48,000 in 2001. Did the company have an increase or decrease in profit from 2001 to 2002?

Since the profit went from $48,000 in 2001 to $54,000 in 2002, the company had an increase in profit.

What was the percent of increase in profit?

Find the percent of increase.

$$\frac{\text{new amount} - \text{original amount}}{\text{original amount}} = \frac{54,000 - 48,000}{48,000}$$

$$= \frac{6,000}{48,000}$$

$$= 0.125$$

$$= 12.5\%$$

The company's profit increased 12.5% from 2001 to 2002.

Practice

1. A company's cost to produce a hook is $2.48. The company sells the hook for $3.99. How much profit does the company make producing and selling 500 hooks?

   _____

2. Marcy's Music sells CDs for $13.99. Best Deal sells CDs for $15.99. Best Deal is having a 20%-off sale. Which store is selling CDs at a cheaper price? How much cheaper are the CDs there?

   _____

3. Darrell's family went to dinner last Saturday night. The total amount of the bill was $58.90. Darrell's dad left the server a 20% tip. He paid for the dinner and tip with his credit card. How much did Darrell's dad leave for a tip? What was the total amount that Darrell's dad charged on his credit card?

   _____

4. The retail price of an aquarium set at Animal Farm is $125. The aquarium sets are on sale at $\frac{2}{5}$ off their retail price. What is the amount of discount and the sale price of an aquarium set at Animal Farm?

   _____

5. A shirt's wholesale price is $12.50 and the store's markup rate is 60%. What is the retail price of the shirt?

   _____

6. Ziggy's subtotal at Gloria's Gifts is $46.80. If there is a 7% sales tax, how much does Ziggy actually pay?

   A. $49.24

   B. $49.66

   C. $50.08

   D. $50.92

7. Jill makes a commission of 12% on each bike she sells. If she sells a bike for $289, how much commission does she make?

   A. $34.68

   B. $35.24

   C. $35.90

   D. $36.46

Interest

Interest is the amount of money that is paid for the use of someone else's money. When you borrow money from the bank, you pay the bank interest to use that money. When you deposit money into an account at the bank, the bank uses your money to invest elsewhere and pays you interest. There are two types of interest that are paid: simple and compound.

Simple interest

Simple interest is paid only on the **principal** (the original amount invested or borrowed), and is paid only at the end of an investment time period. To find simple interest, use this formula:

$I = Prt$ where I = the amount of interest

P = the principal

r = the interest rate

t = the time invested in years

Example

Rebecca deposited $250 into a savings account that pays her simple interest. The interest rate is 8%. How much interest will Rebecca earn in 4 years? What will Rebecca's account balance be after 4 years?

First find the interest earned by substituting the values into the formula and simplifing.

$I = Prt$

$= 250 \cdot 0.08 \cdot 4$

$= 80$

Then find the account balance by adding the principal and the interest.

balance = principal + interest

$= 250 + 80$

$= 330$

After 4 years, Rebecca will earn $80 interest and her account balance will be $330.

Compound interest

Compound interest is paid on the principal and any interest that has already been earned on the money. To find compound interest, use this formula (notice that this formula automatically finds the balance):

$$B = P\left(1 + \frac{r}{n}\right)^{nt}$$ where B = the balance

P = the principal

r = the interest rate

n = the number of times the interest is compounded (added to the balance) each year

t = the time invested in years

When finding compound interest, you need to know how many times the interest is compounded each year. The word **annually** means that the interest is compounded **once** each year, **semiannually** means **twice** each year, and **quarterly** means **four** times each year.

Example

Francine deposited $250 into an account 4 years ago. The account has paid 8% interest compounded annually. What is Francine's account balance?

Substitute the values into the formula and simplify according to the order of operations.

$$B = P\left(1 + \frac{r}{n}\right)^{nt}$$

$$= 250\left(1 + \frac{0.08}{1}\right)^{1 \cdot 4}$$

$$= 250(1.08)^4$$

$$= 250(1.36048896)$$

$$= 340.12224 \approx 340.12$$

Francine's account balance is $340.12.

The more times the interest is compounded each year, the greater the balance will be at the end of the investment time period.

Example

What would Francine's account balance be if the interest was compounded quarterly instead of annually?

$$B = P\left(1 + \frac{r}{n}\right)^{nt}$$

$$= 250\left(1 + \frac{0.08}{4}\right)^{4 \cdot 4}$$

$$= 250(1.02)^{16}$$

$$= 343.1964263\ldots \approx 343.20$$

Francine's account balance would be $343.20.

Practice

1. Jamal deposited $550 into an account that pays 7% simple interest for 3 years. How much simple interest will Jamal earn?

   _____

2. Karen borrowed $350 from Helen. Karen told Helen she would pay her back at a rate of 4% interest compounded semiannually for 5 years. Karen will pay it all back at once. How much will Karen owe Helen after 5 years?

   _____

3. Hyo deposited $250 into an account that pays 8% interest compounded quarterly. How much **interest** will Hyo earn in 10 years?

   _____

4. Hal borrowed $200 from his dad at a rate of 10% simple interest to be paid back in 6 months. How much will Hal have to pay his dad in 6 months?

   A. $205
   B. $210
   C. $220
   D. $260

5. Freddy deposited $500 into an account that pays 6% simple interest for 8 years. How much more interest would Freddy earn if the interest was compounded annually instead of being simple interest?

   A. $56.92
   B. $69.78
   C. $81.64
   D. $95.80

Test Your Skills

1. Nicole earns a 15% commission from magazine sales. Her sales for the month of January were $400. How much commission did Nicole earn for her January sales?

   A. $40
   B. $50
   C. $60
   D. $70

2. Sierra's grandfather was notified of an old savings account that he had forgotten about. Fifty years ago, he deposited $50 into the account at a rate of 8% interest compounded semiannually. What is Sierra's grandfather's account balance?

   A. $665.85
   B. $1,180.45
   C. $1,725.75
   D. $2,525.25

3. A store's 2002 revenue totaled $675,852.36. Its 2002 costs totaled $428,352.36. Its 2001 profit was $278,350. What was the store's percent of increase or decrease in profit from 2001 to 2002?

   A. increase of about 11%
   B. increase of about 14%
   C. decrease of about 11%
   D. decrease of about 14%

4. Derek borrowed $25 from his brother, Craig. Derek has to repay the money in 3 months at 20% simple interest. How much will Derek owe Craig?

   A. $26.25
   B. $27.50
   C. $28.75
   D. $29.00

5. A shoe store's markup rate is $1\frac{1}{4}$ times the wholesale price. What is the retail price of a shoe that has a wholesale price of $22?

   A. $56.25
   B. $49.50
   C. $38.25
   D. $27.50

6. A store is having a $\frac{1}{4}$-off sale on all items. Daniel wants to buy a book that has a retail price of $15. There is a 6% sales tax. What is the total price of the book, including sales tax?

   A. $10.50
   B. $11.13
   C. $11.40
   D. $11.93

Unit 2

Algebra and Functions

Have you ever wondered how a cash register automatically figures the amount of tax that you owe when you make a purchase? Or how a VCR knows what day of the week it will be when you set a date for taping a program?

These are just two of the many ways algebra works in everyday life. Like many machines today, cash registers and VCRs are programmed with algebraic functions that can make instant calculations.

In this unit, you will write, solve, and graph algebraic expressions, equations, inequalities, and linear and nonlinear functions. You will simplify expressions using basic properties and evaluate variable expressions. In addition, you will use slope and other ratios to solve problems.

In This Unit

Expressions, Equations, and Inequalities

Variable Expressions with Exponents

Linear Equations and Functions

Systems of Linear Equations

Quadratic and Cubic Functions

Lesson 4: Expressions, Equations, and Inequalities

Here is a review of a few commonly used algebra terms.

Variable: A **letter** that is used to represent an **unknown number**. The letters used most commonly are *a, b, c, n, x, y,* and *z.*

Constant: A **number** that does not change in value.

Coefficient: A **constant** that is **in front of** a variable. Since the prefix *co* means *with*, remember that a *co*efficient is a constant *with* a variable.

Expression: A collection of constants, variables, grouping symbols, and one or more of the four basic operation signs. Here are some commonly used grouping symbols: parentheses ( ), brackets [ ], and absolute value signs | |. Here is an example of an algebraic expression: $111w + y - 9$.

Term: The individual parts of an expression between the addition or subtraction signs. In the above expression, the terms are $111w$, y, and -9.

Equation: Shows that two expressions are equal by using the *equal sign* (=).

Inequality: Shows that two expressions are **not** equal by using one of the following signs: *greater than* (>), *greater than or equal to* (≥), *less than* (<), or *less than or equal to* (≤). You might also see the *not equal to* sign (≠).

Practice

Directions: For Numbers 1 through 8, identify which of the algebra terms above describes the circled item.

1. ③$n + 4 = 10$ _____

2. ④$(3x - 9)$ ≤ 2 _____

3. $-6$⑨ $= -848$ _____

4. ⑨⑨$q < -396$ _____

5. ③$x - 6 = 39$ _____

6. $x =$ ⑦⓪⓪ _____

7. $3x +$ ⑦y $- 9z$ _____

8. ⑥$y - 7x$ ≥ 28 _____

Evaluating Expressions

Expressions are important components of equations and inequalities. Expressions are often **evaluated**, which means that you substitute given values for the variables in the expression, then follow the order of operations (Lesson 2) to arrive at the solution.

Example

Evaluate: $3(x - 2)$ for $x = 5$

Substitute: $3(x - 2) = 3(5 - 2)$

$$= 3(3)$$

$$= 9$$

Example

Evaluate: $5(8y + 4)^2$ for $y = -2$

Substitute: $5(8y + 4)^2 = 5[8(-2) + 4]^2$

$$= 5[-16 + 4]^2$$

$$= 5(-12)^2$$

$$= 5(144)$$

$$= 720$$

Practice

Directions: For Numbers 1 through 4, substitute the given value(s) for the variable(s) in each expression. Then follow the order of operations to evaluate the expression.

1. $z^2 - 6$ for $z = -3$

2. $a^2 - 3a - 12$ for $a = 4$

3. $3a - 7b$ for $a = -1$ and $b = 4$

4. $-2(2h + 5j - k)$ for $h = 2$, $j = 6$, and $k = -1$

Representing Verbal Descriptions

Sometimes, verbal phrases or sentences are used to express a mathematical relationship. In these cases, all the mathematical information is contained within the phrase or sentence, but you need to translate the English into math. Identifying the "main" operation is often the first step. The main operation shows how the individual terms are linked. Here are the four operations and a few of their related English words or phrases.

Addition: sum, more, more than, plus, increased by, gain, exceed

Subtraction: difference, less, less than, minus, decreased by, loss, diminish

Multiplication: product, of, multiplied by, times, double, triple, quadruple

Division: quotient, divided by, ratio, half, third, fourth

Note: The verbal descriptions *more than* and *less than* switch the order of the terms in the expression from how they appear in the description.

Once you determine the main operation, create all the terms of the expression, equation, or inequality from the remaining words. When other operations are indicated, they will be used to create the individual terms.

Example

Write the correct expression for the following phrase.

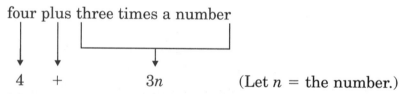

$$4 \quad + \quad 3n \qquad \text{(Let } n = \text{the number.)}$$

What is the main operation? The word *plus* indicates **addition**.

What are the terms to be added? 4 and $3n$

Therefore, "four plus three times a number" is written $4 + 3n$.

You can also write the expression this way: $3n + 4$. When the main operation is addition or multiplication, the order in which you write the terms **does not** matter. (The operations of addition and multiplication are **commutative**.)

When the main operation is subtraction or division, the order in which you write the terms **does** matter.

Example

Write the correct expression for the following phrase.

six less than a number

The phrase *less than* indicates subtraction. Let z = a number.

How do you write the expression: $6 - z$ or $z - 6$?

The word *than* in *less than* tells you to switch the order of the terms in the expression from how they appear in the description.

Therefore, "six less than a number" is written $z - 6$.

In the next example, see if you can figure out what is different from the example above.

Example

Write the correct inequality for the following sentence.

Six is less than a number.

This sentence is different by one tiny word; the word *is* changes everything. Now you'll write an inequality instead of an expression. Let z = a number. The inequality sign points to the smaller number.

Therefore, "six is less than a number" is written $6 < z$ or $z > 6$.

You will review inequalities in greater detail later in this lesson.

Practice

Directions: For Numbers 1 through 5, underline the part of the phrase that indicates the main operation, then write an expression.

1. eight <u>more than</u> a number _____

2. the <u>product</u> of a number and twelve _____

3. four <u>less than</u> six times a number _____

4. eleven <u>decreased</u> by a number _____

5. the sum of a number and nine _____

Directions: For Numbers 6 through 9, find the error(s) in the expression, then write the correct expression on the blank.

6. three less than twice a number: $3 - 2x$ _____

7. the difference of a number and five: $\frac{5}{n}$ _____

8. the quotient of a number and fourteen: $14x$ _____

9. nineteen less than one-third of a number: $19 - 3x$ _____

10. Which phrase translates into the expression $\frac{1}{6}x - 12$?

    A. six times a number minus twelve
    B. twelve less than six times a number
    C. twelve less than one-sixth of a number
    D. twelve decreased by one-sixth of a number

Solving Linear Equations

Linear equations can be solved using the **properties of equality**, which are based on the four operations.

When the same number is **added to** or **subtracted from** both sides of an equation, the two sides of the equation are still equal.

When both sides of an equation are **multiplied by** or **divided by** the same number, the two sides of the equation are still equal. Division by zero is not allowed.

To solve any equation in one variable, follow these steps where necessary:

Step 1: **Use the inverse of any addition or subtraction to isolate the variable term.**

Step 2: **Use the inverse of any multiplication or division.**

Step 3: **Always check your solution using the substitution property.**

 Example

Solve the following linear equation for n.

$$n + 5{,}439 = 439 \qquad \text{(Subtract 5,439 from both sides.)}$$

$$n + 5{,}439 - \mathbf{5{,}439} = 439 - \mathbf{5{,}439}$$

$$n = -5{,}000$$

Check your solution by substituting $-5{,}000$ for n in the original equation.

$$n + 5{,}439 = 439$$

$$\mathbf{-5{,}000} + 5{,}439 = 439$$

$$439 = 439 \ \checkmark$$

The solution is $n = -5{,}000$.

Example

Solve the following linear equation for a.

$$4a - 12 = 6a - 5 \qquad \text{(Subtract } 6a \text{ from both sides.)}$$

$$4a - 12 - \mathbf{6a} = 6a - 5 - \mathbf{6a}$$

$$-2a - 12 = -5 \qquad \text{(Add 12 to both sides.)}$$

$$-2a - 12 + \mathbf{12} = -5 + \mathbf{12}$$

$$-2a = 7 \qquad \text{(Divide both sides by } -2.)$$

$$\frac{-2a}{\mathbf{-2}} = \frac{7}{\mathbf{-2}}$$

$$a = -3.5$$

Check your solution by substituting -3.5 for each a in the original equation.

$$4a - 12 = 6a - 5$$

$$4 \bullet (\mathbf{-3.5}) - 12 = 6 \bullet (\mathbf{-3.5}) - 5$$

$$-14 - 12 = -21 - 5$$

$$-26 = -26 \; \checkmark$$

The solution is $a = -3.5$.

Simplifying linear equations before solving

Sometimes you need to simplify the expressions of a linear equation before you can solve it. To simplify, you might need to use the distributive property and combine like terms.

Distributive property

The distributive property can be used to eliminate parentheses in some expressions. To simplify using the distributive property, multiply each term inside the parentheses by the number on the outside.

Example

Simplify each expression using the distributive property.

$$4(x + 3) = (4 \bullet x) + (4 \bullet 3) = 4x + 12$$

$$3(5 - 2x) = (3 \bullet 5) - (3 \bullet 2x) = 15 - 6x$$

Combining like terms

Like terms have the same variables with the same exponents. Only their coefficients may differ. (All constants are like terms.) Once you find like terms, you can combine them by adding or subtracting their coefficients or the constants.

Example

Simplify each expression by adding the like terms.

$$5x + 3 + 2x + 7 = (5x + 2x) + (3 + 7) = 7x + 10$$

$$2 + 4x - 3x - 8 = (4x - 3x) + (2 - 8) = x - 6$$

After you use the distributive property and combine like terms, you can isolate the variable term on one side of the equation. Then solve for the variable.

Example

Solve the following linear equation for x.

$3(2x + 5) - 5(x + 6) = -30$	(Use the distributive property.)
$6x + 15 - 5x - 30 = -30$	(Add the like terms.)
$x - 15 = -30$	(Add 15 to both sides.)
$x = -15$	

Check your solution by substituting -15 for each x in the original equation.

$$3(2x + 5) - 5(x + 6) = -30$$

$$3[2 \bullet (\mathbf{-15}) + 5] - 5(\mathbf{-15} + 6) = -30$$

$$3(-25) - 5(-9) = -30$$

$$-75 + 45 = -30$$

$$-30 = -30 \ \checkmark$$

The solution is $x = -15$.

Practice

Directions: For Numbers 1 through 12, solve each linear equation. Be sure to check your solution.

1. $5y = 80$

2. $c - 17 = 83$

3. $\dfrac{v}{3} + \dfrac{1}{4} = \dfrac{5}{12}$

4. $31 - 2y = -4y + 3$

5. $4(3z - 5) = 8$

6. $3(4 - 2d) - 2(5d - 5) = 6$

7. $w + 13 = -5$

8. $\dfrac{h}{5} = 0.3$

9. $-7x - 12 = -33$

10. $-15 - 8b = 9b + 28$

11. $2(9a + 6) = -3(a + 17)$

12. $4(3x - 5) + 5(8x - 6) = 26$

Writing and Solving Linear Equations

When you're asked to write a linear equation in one variable from a verbal description (word problem), remember that the word *is* and the phrase *is equal to* are represented by an equal sign. On one side of the equal sign, write an expression to represent the parts of the verbal description **before** *is* or *is equal to*. On the other side of the equal sign, write an expression to represent the parts of the verbal description **after** *is* or *is equal to*. After you have written and solved an equation written from a verbal description, make sure your solution answers the question asked in the problem.

> **Example**
>
> The sum of a number and three times the number is 88. What is the number?
>
> A number: n
>
> Three times the number: $3n$
>
> The sum is 88: $n + 3n = 88$ (Solve for n.)
>
> $$4n = 88$$
>
> $$n = 22$$
>
> Evaluate: $n = 22$
>
> Check: $\mathbf{22} + 3(\mathbf{22}) = 88$
>
> $$22 + 66 = 88$$
>
> $$88 = 88 ✔$$
>
> The number is 22.

> **Example**
>
> A six-pack of soda sells for $2.94. How much does each can of soda cost?
>
> Cost of each can of soda: x
>
> The cost of a six-pack of soda is $2.94: $6x = 2.94$ (Solve for x.)
>
> $$x = 0.49$$
>
> Check: $6 \cdot \mathbf{0.49} = 2.94$
>
> $$2.94 = 2.94 ✔$$
>
> Each can of soda costs $0.49.

Directions: For Numbers 1 through 6, write a linear equation and solve. Be sure to check your solution.

1. Three times a number, decreased by 15, is 60. What is the number?

2. The sum of two consecutive odd integers is 176. What are the two integers?

3. A number divided by 5, increased by 8, is 15. What is the number?

4. Francis, Trudy, Randolf, Vance, and Andrea split a bag of cookies. They each received eight cookies. How many cookies were in the bag?

5. Ethan's age is 8 years more than twice the age of his niece Laurie. If the sum of their ages is 23, what is Laurie's age?

6. The drama club sold $800 worth of tickets for Friday's showing of the school play. Ninety adult tickets and 60 child tickets were sold. The following table shows the ticket prices.

Senior (ages 65 and older)	$2.00
Adult (ages 18–64)	$6.00
Child (ages 17 and younger)	$3.00

How many senior tickets were sold for Friday's show?

Writing and Solving Proportions

A **proportion** states that two ratios are equal. Proportions are useful in many problem-solving situations. In a proportion, the cross products are equal.

Example

Verify that the following proportion is true.

$$\frac{3}{4} = \frac{9}{12}$$

Multiply the numerator of one ratio by the denominator of the other ratio to see if the cross products are equal.

$$3 \cdot 12 = 9 \cdot 4$$
$$36 = 36 \ \checkmark$$

Since the cross products are equal, the proportion is true.

It is extremely important to set up the proportion correctly in a problem-solving situation. The ratios must be written in such a way that the labels on the numerators match and the labels on the denominators match.

Example

During the school recycling week, each student received 10 points for every 6 pounds of newspaper he or she collected. At the end of the week, Phil received 25 points. How many pounds of newspaper did Phil collect?

Set up a proportion. Let n = the number of pounds of newspaper Phil collected.

$$\frac{\text{pounds} \rightarrow}{\text{points} \rightarrow} \frac{6}{10} = \frac{n}{25}$$

Set the cross products equal to each other and solve the linear equation for the variable.

$$10n = 150$$

$$\frac{10n}{10} = \frac{150}{10}$$

$$n = 15$$

Phil collected 15 pounds of newspaper.

Practice

Directions: For Numbers 1 through 4, write a proportion and solve.

1. A 12-ounce box of Corn Muffins cereal costs $2.50. At that rate, how much does an 18-ounce box of Corn Muffins cereal cost?

2. Heather rode her bike 3 miles to Sandy Beach. It took her 45 minutes to get there. When she leaves the beach, she is going to ride 2 miles to Sequoia Park. If Heather's rate of speed is the same on her ride to Sequoia Park as it was to Sandy Beach, how long will it take her to get to Sequoia Park?

3. A company produces 575 gizmos every 5 days. At that rate, how long will it take the company to produce 1,265 gizmos?

4. Horace is on the track team. He ran the 5,000-meter run during the last meet. His average speed was 200 meters per minute. How long did it take Horace to run the 5,000-meter run?

5. The sales tax on a $28 purchase is $1.96. What is the sales tax on a $64.25 purchase?

   A. $4.50
   B. $4.65
   C. $4.80
   D. $4.95

6. A retailer is having a store-wide sale. An item that normally sells for $25 is on sale for $21.25. At that same rate, what is the sale price of an item that normally sells for $35?

   A. $31.25
   B. $30.75
   C. $30.25
   D. $29.75

Writing and Solving Work and Mixture Problems

Work and mixture problems are specific types of problems that you can write as an equation and then solve to find the answer.

Work problems

Work problems use a variation of the distance formula. The work formula is $w = rt$, where w represents the amount of work done, r represents the rate of work, and t represents the time worked.

Example

John can paint a garage in 15 hours. Suzie can paint the same garage in 10 hours. How long would it take for John and Suzie to paint the garage together?

Let t represent the amount of time it takes John and Suzie to paint the garage together.

Find the rate of work for each person per hour. John paints the garage in 15 hours, so he can paint $\frac{1}{15}$ of the garage per hour. Suzie can paint $\frac{1}{10}$ of the garage per hour.

Find the amount of work that each person does.

John: $w = rt$ Suzie: $w = rt$

$\quad = \frac{1}{15}t$ $= \frac{1}{10}t$

Since John and Suzie complete the job, the amount of work that they do together is equal to 1.

$$\frac{1}{15}t + \frac{1}{10}t = 1$$

$$\frac{2}{30}t + \frac{3}{30}t = 1$$

$$\frac{1}{6}t = 1 \qquad \left(\frac{5}{30} = \frac{1}{6}\right)$$

$$t = 6$$

It would take John and Suzie 6 hours to paint the garage together.

Mixture problems

Mixture problems involve adding certain amounts of two or more substances together to create a mixture.

Example

Kim needs a 25% HCl (hydrochloric acid) solution for a science experiment. She has solutions that are 15% HCl and 31% HCl. How much of each kind of solution does Kim need to mix to make 100 mL of 25% HCl solution?

Let x represent the amount of the 15% solution in mL. Then, since the total amount of solution is 100 mL, $100 - x$ represents the amount of the 31% solution in mL.

If you multiply the amount of each solution by the percent of HCl in the solution (written as a decimal), you get the total amount of HCl in each solution. The combined total amount of HCl in the solutions you are mixing equals the total amount of HCl in the mixture.

Sometimes it is easier to show the information in a table.

	Amount of Solution (mL)	% HCl	Total Amount of HCl (mL)
15% Solution	x	0.15	$0.15x$
31% Solution	$100 - x$	0.31	$0.31(100 - x)$
25% Solution	100	0.25	$0.25(100)$

The last column of the table gives you the information to write and solve a linear equation.

$$0.15x + 0.31(100 - x) = 0.25(100)$$
$$0.15x + 31 - 0.31x = 25$$
$$-0.16x = -6$$
$$x = \mathbf{37.5}$$
$$100 - x = 100 - 37.5 = \mathbf{62.5}$$

Kim needs to mix 37.5 mL of the 15% HCl solution with 62.5 mL of the 31% HCl solution to make 100 mL of 25% HCl solution.

Practice

1. Fanny can type 150 words in 3 minutes. Gerard can type 160 words in 4 minutes. How long would it take Fanny and Gerard, working at the same time, to type a 1,800-word report?

2. José can mow and trim 15 lawns in 5 hours. Dave can mow and trim the same 15 lawns in 7.5 hours. How long would it take José and Dave to mow and trim the 15 lawns if they worked together?

3. Dr. Sagan has 50 mL of a 30% saline solution. How many mL of a 60% saline solution must Dr. Sagan add to his solution to produce a 50% saline solution?

	Amount of Solution (mL)	% Saline	Total Amount of Saline (mL)
30% Solution			
60% Solution			
50% Solution			

4. Zilla has 60 g of an alloy that is 10% silver. She mixed it with 40 g of another alloy to make an alloy that is 18% silver. What percent of silver was in the 40 g alloy?

	Amount of Alloy (g)	% Silver	Total Amount of Silver (g)
10% Alloy			
Other Alloy			
18% Alloy			

Solving Linear Inequalities

To solve one-step or multistep linear inequalities ($>$, $<$, $\leq$, or $\geq$), follow the same processes that apply to linear equations (pages 57 through 62). Remember that if you multiply or divide both sides of an inequality by a negative number, you have to switch the inequality sign to the opposite direction.

Example

Solve the following linear inequality for x.

$$\frac{x}{5} + 6 > 15 \qquad \text{(Subtract 6 from both sides.)}$$

$$\frac{x}{5} > 9 \qquad \text{(Multiply both sides by 5.)}$$

$$x > 45$$

Check your solution by substituting any value that satisfies your solution for x in the original inequality, then simplify.

$$\frac{x}{5} + 6 > 15$$

$$\frac{48}{5} + 6 > 15$$

$$15.6 > 15 \quad \text{✔}$$

The solution is $x > 45$.

Example

Solve the following linear inequality for x.

$$-3x - 3 \leq 4x + 39 \qquad \text{(Add 3 to and subtract } 4x \text{ from both sides.)}$$

$$-7x \leq 42 \qquad \text{(Divide both sides by } -7 \text{ and switch the sign.)}$$

$$x \geq -6$$

Check your solution.

$$-3x - 3 \leq 4x + 39$$

$$-3 \bullet (-3) - 3 \leq 4 \bullet (-3) + 39$$

$$6 \leq 27 \quad \text{✔}$$

The solution is $x \geq -6$.

Graphing linear inequalities

Unlike linear equations, most linear inequalities have an infinite number of solutions. The graph of a linear inequality represents the solutions. The graph shows an open or a closed dot on the number line; the number line is shaded on one side or the other of the dot. There is an **open dot** if the sign from the solution is either $<$ **or** $>$; there is a **closed dot** if the sign from the solution is either $\leq$ **or** $\geq$. The part of the number line that is shaded will show the numbers that can be substituted for the variable in the inequality to make the inequality true.

Example

Graph the linear inequality: $-3x - 3 \leq 4x + 39$

The solution of the inequality $-3x - 3 \leq 4x + 39$ was found on page 68 to be $x \geq -6$. The following is the graph of the solutions of the inequality.

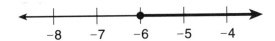

Since -6 and any number greater than -6 can be substituted for x in the inequality $-3x - 3 \leq 4x + 39$ to make it true, the -6 has a closed dot, and the number line is shaded to the right of -6.

Practice

Directions: For Numbers 1 through 8, solve each linear inequality. Be sure to check your solution. Then draw a graph of the solutions of the inequality.

1. $9x + 13 \leq 4 - (-6x)$

2. $-\frac{1}{2}w + 4 > -3$

3. $36.4 + 1.2a \geq 44.44$

4. $\frac{2}{3}z - \frac{1}{6} \leq \frac{1}{2} - \frac{1}{6}z$

5. $-8(c - 2) > 40$

6. $4(2s + 3) > 5(s - 6)$

7. $-2(4 - 7t) < -6(3t + 4)$

8. $6(2t - 8) + 3(t + 5) \leq 2$

Writing and Solving Linear Inequalities

Sometimes the difference between a linear equation and a linear inequality is hard to spot in word problems. Here are a few phrases that suggest an inequality rather than an equation.

is at least, is more than, is less than, is greater than

Example

Write a linear inequality and solve: Three less than the quantity nine times a number is at least 75. What is the number?

$$9x - 3 \geq 75 \qquad \text{(Add 3 to both sides.)}$$

$$9x \geq 78 \qquad \text{(Divide both sides by 9.)}$$

$$x \geq 8\frac{2}{3}$$

Check your solution by substituting any value that satisfies your solution for x in the original equation, then simplify.

$$9x - 3 \geq 75$$

$$9 \cdot 9 - 3 \geq 75$$

$$81 - 3 \geq 75$$

$$78 \geq 75 \ ✔$$

The number is greater than or equal to $8\frac{2}{3}$.

Example

Tommy has $60. He wants to buy a $15 rugby shirt and as many $8 T-shirts as he can. What is the greatest number of T-shirts Tommy can buy?

Write an inequality and solve.

$$8x + 15 \leq 60 \qquad \text{(Subtract 15 from both sides.)}$$

$$8x \leq 45 \qquad \text{(Divide both sides by 8.)}$$

$$x \leq 5\frac{5}{8}$$

Check your solution.

$$8x + 15 \leq 60$$

$$8 \cdot 5 + 15 \leq 60$$

$$55 \leq 60 \ ✔$$

The greatest number of T-shirts Tommy can buy is 5 (the number of shirts must be a whole number).

Practice

Directions: For Numbers 1 through 6, write a linear inequality and solve. Be sure to check your solution.

1. One-fourth of a number, increased by $\frac{3}{8}$, is less than or equal to $\frac{1}{16}$.

2. The product of four and a number, decreased by 8.42, is at least 12.58.

3. The quotient of a number and 3, increased by $\frac{5}{6}$, is less than 2.

4. A number multiplied by $2\frac{3}{5}$, decreased by $\frac{1}{10}$, is greater than $\frac{3}{4}$.

5. A roll of insulation covers 100 ft^2 of surface. Polly is insulating the attic of her house, which is 1,350 ft^2. What is the least number of rolls Polly will need to buy to insulate her attic?

6. A zoo charges an admission price of $85 for the first 12 members of a group and $6 for each additional member of the group. What is the largest group that can go to the zoo and spend less than $155 on admission?

Solving Absolute Value Equations and Inequalities

Although absolute value equations and inequalities are not linear, the process for solving them includes solving linear equations or inequalities. Remember that the absolute value of a number is defined as its distance from zero on a number line, and that it is always positive or zero ($|x| \geq 0$). If $|x| = 3$, then the solutions are $x = 3$ and $x = -3$, because both 3 and -3 are three units from zero on the number line. The same thought process is used when you solve multistep absolute value equations and inequalities.

To solve an absolute value equation:

- isolate the absolute value term on the left side of the equal sign

- write two different equations separated by "or," one setting the absolute value expression equal to the number and another setting it equal to the **opposite** of the number

- solve each linear equation and check each solution

The solutions are sometimes written using set notation, { }. The solutions $x = 3$ and $x = -3$ can be written as the solution set $\{-3, 3\}$.

> **Example**
>
> Solve for x: $|3x - 8| = 4$
>
> $|3x - 8| = 4$ (The absolute value term is isolated; set up the two equations.)
>
> $$3x - 8 = 4 \qquad \text{or} \qquad 3x - 8 = -4 \quad \text{(Solve the equations.)}$$
>
> $$3x = 12 \qquad\qquad\qquad 3x = 4$$
>
> $$x = 4 \qquad\qquad\qquad x = 1\tfrac{1}{3}$$
>
> Check your solutions.
>
> $$|3 \cdot 4 - 8| = 4 \qquad \text{and} \qquad |3 \cdot 1\tfrac{1}{3} - 8| = 4$$
>
> $$|12 - 8| = 4 \qquad\qquad\qquad |4 - 8| = 4$$
>
> $$|4| = 4 \qquad\qquad\qquad\qquad |-4| = 4$$
>
> $$4 = 4 \; ✔ \qquad\qquad\qquad\qquad 4 = 4 \; ✔$$
>
> The solutions are $x = 4$ and $x = 1\tfrac{1}{3}$. The solution set is $\left\{1\tfrac{1}{3}, 4\right\}$.

To solve an absolute value inequality, follow the same steps as for solving absolute value equations, except when you separate the original inequality into two different inequalities. If the original inequality is in the form $|ax + b| < c$, separate the inequalities with "and." If the original inequality is in the form $|ax + b| > c$, separate the inequalities with "or." Also, when writing the inequality using the opposite of the number on the right, flip the inequality sign in either case. The same rules apply for ≤ and ≥. A graph is helpful for giving a visual representation of the solution.

Example

Solve for y: $|4y - 6| - 3 > 11$

$|4y - 6| - 3 > 11$ (Add 3 to both sides.)

$|4y - 6| > 14$ (Set up the two inequalities, separated by "or.")

$4y - 6 > 14$ or $4y - 6 < -14$ (Solve the inequalities.)

$4y > 20$ $4y < -8$

$y > 5$ $y < -2$

Check your solutions.

$|4 \cdot \mathbf{6} - 6| - 3 > 11$ and $|4 \cdot (\mathbf{-4}) - 6| - 3 > 11$

$|24 - 6| - 3 > 11$ $|-16 - 6| - 3 > 11$

$|18| - 3 > 11$ $|-22| - 3 > 11$

$18 - 3 > 11$ $22 - 3 > 11$

$15 > 11$ ✔ $19 > 11$ ✔

The solutions are $y > 5$ or $y < -2$.

The following is the graph of the solution of the inequality.

Directions: For Numbers 1 through 6, solve each absolute value equation or inequality. Be sure to check your solutions. Then draw a graph of the solutions of each inequality.

1. $|4 - w| = 5$

2. $|3c - 8| < 7$

3. $|2b - 8| - 6 = 2$

4. $|t + 9| \geq 7$

5. $|7r + 3| \leq 4$

6. $3|v| - 4 = 11$

Test Your Skills

1. One half of some number increased by 9 is 17. What is the number?

   A.　4
   B.　8
   C. 12
   D. 16

2. What is the solution of the following linear inequality?

   $$-6x - 9 > -33$$

   A. $x > -4$
   B. $x < -4$
   C. $x > 4$
   D. $x < 4$

3. The sum of two consecutive odd integers is 48. Which linear equation represents the sum?

   A. $x + (x + 1) = 48$
   B. $x + (x + 2) = 48$
   C. $x(x + 1) = 48$
   D. $x(x + 2) = 48$

4. What are the solutions of the following absolute value equation?

   $$|-2x - 4| - 3 = 9$$

   A. $x = -4$ and $x = 8$
   B. $x = -8$ and $x = 4$
   C. $x = -12$ and $x = 6$
   D. $x = -6$ and $x = 12$

5. Kurt has $80. He wants to buy a $15 DVD and as many $10 CDs as he can. The following linear inequality represents the information, where c is the number of CDs that Kurt can buy.

   $$10c + 15 \le 80$$

   Which phrase **best** describes the number of CDs Kurt can buy?

   A. at most 6
   B. at least 6
   C. less than 6
   D. more than 6

6. Evaluate the following expression for $x = 2$, $y = -3$, and $z = 4$.

   $$4xy - 2z + 3$$

   A. 29
   B. 13
   C. −13
   D. −29

7. Which linear inequality represents the following sentence?

   Twice a number, increased by three, is less than or equal to seven.

   A. $2x + 3 \ge 7$
   B. $2x + 3 \le 7$
   C. $2(x + 3) \le 7$
   D. $2(x + 3) \ge 7$

8. Which linear inequality is equivalent to the following?

$$3(2x - 4) - 5(3x - 7) \geq 5$$

A. $-9x + 23 \geq 5$
B. $-9x - 47 \geq 5$
C. $21x + 23 \geq 5$
D. $21x - 47 \geq 5$

9. Which graph shows the solution of the following linear inequality?

$$-5x - 8 < -2.5$$

A.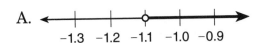

B.

C.

D.

10. Which phrase represents the following expression?

$$6 - 4y$$

A. the product of four and a number, minus six
B. six minus the quotient of four and a number
C. the product of four and a number, less than six
D. six less than the quotient of four and a number

11. One machine can print 250 pamphlets in 100 minutes. Another machine can print 270 of the same pamphlets in 90 minutes. How long would it take both machines, working at the same time, to print 8,250 pamphlets?

A.   750 minutes
B. 1,500 minutes
C. 1,650 minutes
D. 3,000 minutes

12. Jamie drove 180 miles in 4.5 hours. At that rate, how far can Jamie drive in 6 hours?

A. 135 miles
B. 175 miles
C. 240 miles
D. 270 miles

13. What is the solution of the following linear equation?

$$-5y + 7 = -4 - 9y$$

A. $y = -2\frac{3}{4}$

B. $y = -\frac{3}{14}$

C. $y = \frac{11}{14}$

D. $y = 1\frac{3}{4}$

Lesson 5: Variable Expressions with Exponents

In Lessons 1 and 2, you reviewed how to simplify numerical expressions that have exponents. In this lesson, you will apply the same rules to variable expressions that have positive or negative integer exponents. You will also review computation of polynomials, including the rules for exponents.

Positive Exponents

Positive exponents can be interpreted as repeated multiplication. For example, $x^5 = x \cdot x \cdot x \cdot x \cdot x$. To simplify $(3y)^4$, multiply using the term inside the ( ) as a factor the number of times shown by the exponent (^{4}).

$$(3y)^4 = 3y \cdot 3y \cdot 3y \cdot 3y = 3^4 \cdot y^4 = 81y^4$$

Remember that a variable that doesn't show a coefficient (number in front) actually has a coefficient of 1.

To evaluate variable expressions, substitute a given value into the expression, follow the order of operations, and solve.

Example

Evaluate the expression $2x^3 + 5$ for $x = 4$.

Substitute: $2x^3 + 5 = 2(4)^3 + 5$

$$= 2(64) + 5$$
$$= 128 + 5$$
$$= 133$$

Example

Evaluate the expression $3z^2 - 8z$ for $z = -6$.

Substitute: $3z^2 - 8z = 3(-6)^2 - 8(-6)$

$$= 3(36) - 8(-6)$$
$$= 108 + 48$$
$$= 156$$

Negative Exponents

Negative exponents can be interpreted as **repeated division**. So what do you do when you see a negative exponent? You write the reciprocal of the base (its multiplicative inverse) and rewrite the exponent on the base as its opposite.

Example

Simplify: x^{-5}

Since the exponent is negative, write the reciprocal of the base and rewrite the exponent as its opposite.

$$x^{-5} = \frac{1}{x^5}$$

To evaluate expressions with negative exponents, first rewrite any bases with negative exponents to bases with positive exponents. Then substitute, follow the order of operations, and simplify.

Example

Evaluate $2y^{-3}$ for $y = 4$.

Rewrite the negative exponent: $2y^{-3} = \frac{2}{y^3}$

Substitute: $\frac{2}{y^3} = \frac{2}{4^3}$

$$= \frac{2}{64}$$

$$= \frac{1}{32}$$

 TIP: Remember that there is an important difference between $7x^{-3}$ and $(7x)^{-3}$. $7x^{-3}$ means $\frac{7}{x^3}$, while $(7x)^{-3}$ means $\left(\frac{1}{7x}\right)^3$.

Practice

Directions: For Numbers 1 through 3, evaluate each expression for $x = 6$, $y = 3$, and $z = -4$.

1. $xy^2 + z$ $9x^{-2} + 6y^{-3}$

2. $x^3 + 6y^2$ $(7x^{-2})(6y^{-2})$

3. $z - 3x^2$ $8x^2z^{-3}$

4. For what values of a and b is the following expression equal to 46?

   $5a + 3b$

   A. $a = 5; b = 6$
   B. $a = 7; b = 10$
   C. $a = 8; b = 2$
   D. $a = 9; b = 1$

5. Which expression is equivalent to $8m^{-3}$?

   A. $\left(\dfrac{8}{m}\right)^3$

   B. $\dfrac{8}{m^3}$

   C. $\dfrac{m^3}{8}$

   D. $\left(\dfrac{m}{8}\right)^3$

Monomials

A **monomial** is a constant, a variable, or the product of one or more constants and one or more variables.

Adding or subtracting monomials

When adding or subtracting monomials, they must be like terms, which you read about in Lesson 4.

$3a^4b$ and $-5a^4b$ are like terms.

$4x^7yz^5$ and $2x^5yz^7$ are **not** like terms.

To add or subtract like terms, add or subtract the coefficients while leaving the bases (variables) and exponents as they are. The distributive property allows you to add or subtract the coefficients.

Example

Add: $8a^3b^2 + (-5a^3b^2)$

These are like terms, so add the coefficients and leave the bases and the exponents as they are.

$$8a^3b^2 + (-5a^3b^2) = \left[8 + (-5)\right]a^3b^2 = 3a^3b^2$$

Therefore, $8a^3b^2 + (-5a^3b^2) = 3a^3b^2$.

Example

Subtract: $-6xy^4z^2 - xy^4z^2$

Again, these are like terms, so subtract the coefficients (the second term has a coefficient of 1 that is not written) and leave the bases and the exponents as they are.

$$-6xy^4z^2 - xy^4z^2 = (-6 - 1)xy^4z^2 = -7xy^4z^2$$

Therefore, $-6xy^4z^2 - xy^4z^2 = -7xy^4z^2$.

Multiplying monomials

When multiplying monomials, multiply the coefficients and add the exponents of the like bases (variables). The associative and commutative properties allow you to regroup and switch the order of the terms in the multiplication.

Example

Multiply: $(-3x^4)(2x)$

Remember that the exponent of the x in $2x$ is 1.

$$(-3x^4)(2x) = (-3 \cdot 2)(x^{4 + 1}) = -6x^5$$

Therefore, $(-3x^4)(2x) = -6x^5$.

Example

Multiply: $(-4x^5y^2)(x^8y^7)$

$$(-4x^5y^2)(x^8y^7) = (-4 \cdot 1)(x^{5 + 8})(y^{2 + 7}) = -4x^{13}y^9$$

Therefore, $(-4x^5y^2)(x^8y^7) = -4x^{13}y^9$.

Dividing monomials

When dividing monomials, reduce the coefficients (write them in lowest terms) and subtract the exponents (larger − smaller) of the like bases (variables). Put the base and its new exponent in the numerator or denominator, wherever the larger exponent originally was. (In the following examples, the bases with the larger exponents are shown in bold-faced type.)

Example

Divide: $\dfrac{9a^4\boldsymbol{b^7}c}{12a^4b^4\boldsymbol{c^3}}$

Remember, if you don't see an exponent on a variable, the exponent is 1.

$$\frac{9a^4\boldsymbol{b^7}c}{12a^4b^4\boldsymbol{c^3}} = \frac{9}{12} \cdot \frac{a^{4 - 4}b^{7 - 4}}{c^{3 - 1}} = \frac{3b^3}{4c^2} \qquad (a^{4 - 4} = a^0 = 1)$$

Therefore, $\dfrac{9a^4\boldsymbol{b^7}c}{12a^4b^4\boldsymbol{c^3}} = \dfrac{3b^3}{4c^2}$.

If all the bases (variables) with the larger exponents are in the numerator or denominator, write a 1 where the bases (variables) with the smaller exponents were.

Example

Divide: $\frac{2a^4b^2}{6a^6b^3}$

$$\frac{2a^4b^2}{6a^6b^3} = \frac{2}{6} \bullet \frac{1}{a^{6-4}b^{3-2}} = \frac{1}{3a^2b}$$

Therefore, $\frac{2a^4b^2}{6a^6b^3} = \frac{1}{3a^2b}$.

Monomials raised to a power

When raising a monomial to a power, raise the coefficient to the power and multiply each exponent of the bases (variables) by the power.

Example

Simplify: $(-4d^2e^3)^5$

$$(-4d^2e^3)^5 = (-4)^5(d^{2 \bullet 5})(e^{3 \bullet 5}) = -1{,}024d^{10}e^{15}$$

Therefore, $(-4d^2e^3)^5 = -1{,}024d^{10}e^{15}$.

Example

Simplify: $(3x^3y^2z^4)^3$

$$(3x^3y^2z^4)^3 = (3)^3(x^{3 \bullet 3})(y^{2 \bullet 3})(z^{4 \bullet 3}) = 27x^9y^6z^{12}$$

Therefore, $(3x^3y^2z^4)^3 = 27x^9y^6z^{12}$.

Practice

Directions: For Numbers 1 through 8, add or subtract the monomials.

1. $-5x^3y^2 + (-9x^3y^2)$

2. $7u^7v^5 - (-3u^7v^5)$

3. $13j^2k^9l - j^2k^9l$

4. $-3z^{12} + 3z^{12}$

5. $-8x^5y^5 + (-5x^5y^5)$

6. $7x^2z^3 - 2y^2z^3$

7. $6a^3b^9c - (-4a^3b^9c)$

8. $-r^7s^2t^3 + (-2r^7s^2t^3)$

Directions: For Numbers 9 through 16, multiply the monomials.

9. $(3x^3y^2)(-6xy^7)$

10. $(-a^6b^7)(-3b^7c^5)$

11. $(16g^4h^3i^8)(3ghi)$

12. $(-3x^7y^2z^9)(4z^2)$

13. $(-a^4b^2c^8)(a^4b^2c^8)$

14. $(4a^2b^3)(9x^4y^2z^7)$

15. $(5a^3b^7c^9)(-5ab^2c^3d)$

16. $(-8f^7g^3h)(2f^2g^9h^2)$

Directions: For Numbers 17 through 24, divide the monomials.

17. $\dfrac{x^5 y^2}{x^3 y^7}$

21. $\dfrac{12 x^4 y^3}{15 x^4 y^7 z^3}$

18. $\dfrac{4 a^3 b^5 c^2}{14 a b^2 c}$

22. $\dfrac{-17 a^2 b^2 c^5 d}{34 a^3 b^5 c^5 d^3}$

19. $\dfrac{-5 x^2 y^3 z}{-6 y^5 z^3}$

23. $\dfrac{27 a^4 b^3 c}{18 a^2 b^8 c^3}$

20. $\dfrac{8 a^4 b^2}{-12 a^4 b^2}$

24. $\dfrac{-f^7 g^4 h^2}{-5 f^8 g^2 h^4}$

Directions: For Numbers 25 through 32, simplify the monomials.

25. $(6 a^4 g^2)^3$

29. $(8 x^5 y^7 z^6)^4$

26. $(-5 x^4 y)^6$

30. $\left(\dfrac{1}{4} v^5 w^8\right)^4$

27. $(-9 f^7 g^5 h^4)^3$

31. $(r^7 s^2 t)^6$

28. $(-7 w)^4$

32. $\left(-\dfrac{2}{5} j^2 k^6 l^3\right)^4$

Perfect squares

A **perfect square** monomial has a **perfect square coefficient** and **even exponents** on every variable. The numbers 1, 4, 9, 16, 25, 36, . . . are perfect squares.

To simplify the square root ($\sqrt{}$) of a monomial, find the square root of the coefficient and divide the exponent(s) of the variable(s) by 2. Since each perfect square has two roots, one positive and one negative, which one will you use? In most cases, you will use the principal square root.

Example

Simplify: $\sqrt{49a^8b^4}$

Check to be sure that this monomial is a perfect square. Is its coefficient a perfect square and are all its exponents even? Since the answer to this question is yes, the monomial is a perfect square. Find the square root of the coefficient and divide the exponents by 2.

$$\sqrt{49a^8b^4} = \sqrt{7^2 a^{2 \cdot 4} b^{2 \cdot 2}} = 7a^4b^2$$

Therefore, $\sqrt{49a^8b^4} = 7a^4b^2$.

Example

Simplify: $\sqrt{x^6y^{10}}$

The coefficient of this monomial is 1, which is a perfect square. All the exponents are even. This is a perfect square monomial. Find the square root of the coefficient and divide the exponents by 2.

$$\sqrt{x^6y^{10}} = \sqrt{1^2 x^{2 \cdot 3} y^{2 \cdot 5}} = x^3y^5$$

Therefore, $\sqrt{x^6y^{10}} = x^3y^5$.

Perfect cubes

A **perfect cube** monomial has a **perfect cube coefficient** and **exponents** that are **multiples of three**. The numbers . . . , $-27, -8, -1, 0, 1, 8, 27, . . .$ are perfect cubes. The perfect cubes are the numbers that are formed when a number (the cube root) occurs as a factor three times.

To simplify the cube root ($\sqrt[3]{}$) of a monomial, find the cube root of the coefficient and divide the exponent(s) of the variable(s) by 3.

Example

Simplify: $\sqrt[3]{125x^3y^9}$

Check to be sure that this monomial is a perfect cube. Is its coefficient a perfect cube and are all its exponents multiples of 3? Since the answer to this question is yes, the monomial is a perfect cube. Find the cube root of the coefficient and divide the exponents by 3.

$$\sqrt[3]{125x^3y^9} = \sqrt[3]{5^3x^{3 \cdot 1}y^{3 \cdot 3}} = 5xy^3$$

Therefore, $\sqrt[3]{125x^3y^9} = 5xy^3$.

There are times when a perfect cube coefficient is negative. In this case, the cube root will also be negative.

Example

Simplify: $\sqrt[3]{-8a^6b^{12}}$

The coefficient of this monomial is -8, which is a perfect cube. All the exponents are multiples of 3. This is a perfect cube monomial. Find the cube root of the coefficient and divide the exponents by 3.

$$\sqrt[3]{-8a^6b^{12}} = \sqrt[3]{(-2)^3a^{3 \cdot 2}b^{3 \cdot 4}} = -2a^2b^4$$

Therefore, $\sqrt[3]{-8a^6b^{12}} = -2a^2b^4$.

Practice

Directions: For Numbers 1 through 12, simplify the monomials.

1. $\sqrt{a^8 b^4}$

2. $\sqrt[3]{r^3 s^6}$

3. $\sqrt[3]{-216 x^6 y^9}$

4. $\sqrt{25 z^{12}}$

5. $\sqrt{81 h^4}$

6. $\sqrt[3]{1,000 a^9 b^3 c^{18}}$

7. $\sqrt[3]{343 j^9 k^{12} l^3}$

8. $\sqrt{144 b^8 c^{12}}$

9. $\sqrt{4 x^4 y^8 z^{16}}$

10. $\sqrt[3]{-729 x^{12} y^{24}}$

11. $\sqrt[3]{\dfrac{1}{64} a^6 b^9}$

12. $\sqrt{\dfrac{64}{121} r^2 s^6}$

Polynomials

A **polynomial** is a monomial or the sum of monomials. Each monomial of a polynomial is called a **term** of the polynomial. A polynomial with two terms is called a **binomial**. A polynomial with three terms is called a **trinomial**. The terms of a polynomial are usually written in **standard form**: decreasing order of the exponents of the variable or of **one** of the variables.

Adding polynomials

To add polynomials, add the like terms of the polynomials.

Example

Add: $(4x^3 + 7x^2 - 5x) + (-9x^2 + 6x)$

The like terms are the x^2 and x terms. Since there is no term with which to add the x^3 term, it will stay the same.

$$(4x^3 + 7x^2 - 5x) + (-9x^2 + 6x) = 4x^3 + [7x^2 + (-9x^2)] + (-5x + 6x)$$
$$= 4x^3 - 2x^2 + x$$

Therefore, $(4x^3 + 7x^2 - 5x) + (-9x^2 + 6x) = 4x^3 - 2x^2 + x$.

Subtracting polynomials

To subtract polynomials, add the opposite. Change the $-$ between the polynominals to $+$ and change **every** term in the second polynomial to its opposite, then follow the rule for addition.

Example

Subtract: $(x - 6) - (4x^2 - 7x + 5)$

Change $-$ to $+$ and change each term of $4x^2 - 7x + 5$ to its opposite. Then add.

$$(x - 6) - (4x^2 - 7x + 5) = (x - 6) + (-4x^2 + 7x - 5)$$
$$= -4x^2 + (x + 7x) + [-6 + (-5)]$$
$$= -4x^2 + 8x - 11$$

Therefore, $(x - 6) - (4x^2 - 7x + 5) = -4x^2 + 8x - 11$.

Multiplying polynomials

To multiply polynomials, use a form of the distributive property. Multiply **each** term of the first polynomial by **each** term of the second polynomial, then combine the like terms when appropriate.

Example

Multiply: $5w(7w^2 - 8w + 3)$

Multiply $5w$ by each term of $7w^2 - 8w + 3$. Follow the rules for multiplying monomials.

$$5w(7w^2 - 8w + 3) = (5w \bullet 7w^2) - (5w \bullet 8w) + (5w \bullet 3)$$
$$= 35w^3 - 40w^2 + 15w$$

Therefore, $5w(7w^2 - 8w + 3) = 35w^3 - 40w^2 + 15w$.

Example

Multiply: $(3x + 4)(4x^2 - 6x + 2)$

Multiply $3x$ by each term of $4x^2 - 6x + 2$. Then multiply 4 by each term of $4x^2 - 6x + 2$. Finally, combine the like terms.

$$(3x + 4)(4x^2 - 6x + 2) = 12x^3 - 18x^2 + 6x + 16x^2 - 24x + 8$$
$$= 12x^3 - 2x^2 - 18x + 8$$

Therefore, $(3x + 4)(4x^2 - 6x + 2) = 12x^3 - 2x^2 - 18x + 8$.

When multiplying two binomials, you can use the acronym **FOIL** (**F**irst, **O**uter, **I**nner, **L**ast) to help you remember what terms to multiply.

Example

Multiply: $(x - 5)(2x + 3)$

Use the FOIL technique to multiply the binomials.

$$(x - 5)(2x + 3) = 2x^2 + 3x - 10x - 15$$
$$= 2x^2 - 7x - 15$$

Therefore, $(x - 5)(2x + 3) = 2x^2 - 7x - 15$.

Dividing polynomials

To divide polynomials, use a process similar to long division of real numbers. As with place value in real numbers, make sure you keep the terms lined up.

Example

Divide: $(6x^3 - 2x^2 + 8x) \div 2x$

Set up the division similar to long division of a three-digit real number by a one-digit real number.

$$
\begin{array}{r}
3x^2 - x + 4 \\
2x{\overline{\smash{\big)}\,6x^3 - 2x^2 + 8x}} \\
\underline{-6x^3} \\
-2x^2 \\
\underline{-(-2x^2)} \\
8x \\
\underline{-8x} \\
0
\end{array}
$$

Therefore, $(6x^3 - 2x^2 + 8x) \div 2x = 3x^2 - x + 4$.

Example

Divide: $(2x^2 + x - 15) \div (x + 3)$

Set it up as a long division problem.

$$
\begin{array}{r}
2x - 5 \\
x + 3{\overline{\smash{\big)}\,2x^2 + x - 15}} \\
\underline{-(2x^2 + 6x)} \\
-5x - 15 \\
\underline{-(-5x - 15)} \\
0
\end{array}
$$

Therefore, $(2x^2 + x - 15) \div (x + 3) = 2x - 5$.

Practice

Directions: For Numbers 1 through 6, add or subtract the polynomials.

1. $(6x^2y - 4xy^2) + (-9x^2y - 7xy^2)$

2. $(6x^2y - 4xy^2) - (-9x^2y - 7xy^2)$

3. $(5y^3 + 8y^2 - 6) + (9y^3 - 2y^2 + 3y)$

4. $(5y^3 + 8y^2 - 6) - (9y^3 - 2y^2 + 3y)$

5. $(4x^4 + 3x^3y - 5xy^3) + (-7x^4 - 9x^2y^2 + y^4)$

6. $(4x^4 + 3x^3y - 5xy^3) - (-7x^4 - 9x^2y^2 + y^4)$

Directions: For Numbers 7 through 12, multiply or divide the polynomials.

7. $(3x - 6)(2x + 9)$

8. $(4x^3 - 6x^2 + 12x) \div 2x$

9. $(3y^3 + 11y^2 - 25y - 25) \div (y + 5)$

10. $(3x^2 - 5)(x^3 + 6x^2 - 8x + 3)$

11. $4x^2y^3(6x^2 - 5xy + y^2)$

12. $(3x^3 - 7x^2 + 11x - 3) \div (x^2 - 2x + 3)$

Applications with Polynomials

You can use computation with polynomials in problem-solving situations. In some cases, it may be helpful to use models.

Example

The floor of John's garage was square. He then built an addition onto the garage. The addition added 4 ft to the length of the garage and 5 feet to the width of the garage. What polynomial represents the area of the garage with the new addition?

The dimensions of the original garage are not given, but the garage was square. Therefore, label each of the original dimensions x. Add the dimensions of the addition to the garage.

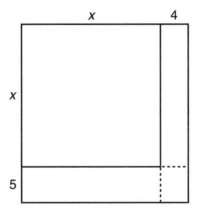

Multiply to find the area of each section of the garage with the addition.

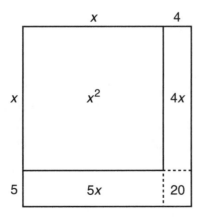

Find the area of the garage with the addition by adding the areas of the sections.

$$x^2 + 4x + 5x + 20 = x^2 + 9x + 20$$

The area of the garage with the addition is $x^2 + 9x + 20$.

Practice

1. Bob wants to add on to his workout room. It is now 15 ft by 18 ft. He is going to add on the same length (x) to both dimensions. What polynomial represents the amount of floor space that Bob will **add** to his workout room?

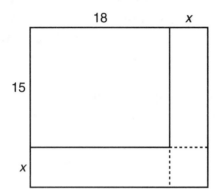

2. Louise has a rectangular pool in her backyard. The length of the pool is 3 times the width of the pool. All the way around the pool there is a pool deck with a total width that is twice the width of the pool and a total length that is 12 ft more than the length of the pool. What polynomial represents the area of the pool deck?

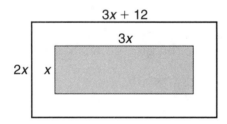

3. Jack, Jeremy, and Jimmy are brothers. Jack is x years old. Jeremy is eight years less than 3 times as old as Jack. Jimmy is 2 times as old as Jeremy. What polynomials represent the ages of Jeremy and Jimmy? What polynomial represents the combined ages of the three brothers?

Test Your Skills

1. Simplify:

$$\frac{8x^4y^2z^3}{(-4x^2y^3z)(6x^4y^5)}$$

   A. $-\dfrac{z^2}{3x^2y^6}$

   B. $-\dfrac{x^2z^2}{3y^6}$

   C. $-3x^2y^6z^2$

   D. $-\dfrac{x^2z^2}{16y^6}$

2. Divide:

$$\frac{-16x^4y^5z^2}{32x^8yz^2}$$

   A. $-2x^4y^4$

   B. $-\dfrac{y^4z}{2x^4}$

   C. $-\dfrac{y^5z}{2x^2}$

   D. $-\dfrac{y^4}{2x^4}$

3. Simplify:

$$\sqrt[3]{-8a^6b^{12}}$$

   A. $-2a^3b^6$
   B. $-2a^2b^4$
   C. $2a^3b^6$
   D. $2a^2b^4$

4. Subtract:

$$(3x^2 + 4x + 6) - (-x^2 + 5x + 7)$$

   A. $4x^2 - x - 1$
   B. $-4x^2 + x + 1$
   C. $2x^2 + 9x + 13$
   D. $-4x - 9x - 13$

5. Multiply:

$$(3x + 6)(x^2 - 5x + 9)$$

   A. $3x^3 + 6x^2 + x + 54$
   B. $3x^3 - 9x^2 + 15x + 3$
   C. $3x^3 + 6x^2 + 9x + 15$
   D. $3x^3 - 9x^2 - 3x + 54$

6. Add:

$$(4x^2 + 4y^2) + (6y^2 - 8x^2)$$

   A. $-2x^2 - 4y^2$
   B. $10x^2 + 4y^2$
   C. $-4x^2 + 10y^2$
   D. $12x^2 - 10y^2$

7. Evaluate the following expression for $x = 2$.

$$4x^{-3}$$

   A. $\dfrac{1}{512}$

   B. $\dfrac{1}{2}$

   C. 2

   D. 32

8. Simplify:

$$4(2x^2 + 3x - 5) + 2x(3x - 6)$$

A. $14x^2 - 20$
B. $8x^2 + 18x - 8$
C. $8x^2 + 18x - 32$
D. $14x^2 + 12x - 32$

9. Simplify:

$$(-4m^4n^2)^3$$

A. $-12m^{12}n^6$
B. $-12m^7n^5$
C. $-64m^{12}n^6$
D. $-64m^7n^5$

10. Divide:

$$(6x^2 - x - 35) \div (3x + 7)$$

A. $3x + 5$
B. $3x - 6$
C. $2x + 6$
D. $2x - 5$

11. Multiply:

$$(4x^2y)(-3x^4y^5)$$

A. $-12x^6y^5$
B. $-12x^6y^6$
C. $-12x^8y^5$
D. $-12x^8y^6$

12. Claire has an 8 in. by 10 in. picture that she wants to frame. She will use matting around the outside of the picture between the picture and the frame. The width of the matting around the picture is the same at the top, bottom, and each side.

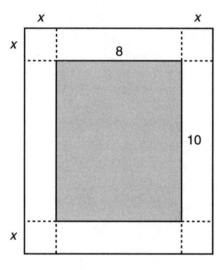

What polynomial represents the area of the matting?

A. $2x^2 + 80x$
B. $2x^2 + 36x$
C. $4x^2 + 36x$
D. $4x^2 + 80x$

13. Simplify:

$$\sqrt{64x^{16}y^2}$$

A. $8x^8y$
B. $4x^4y^2$
C. $-8x^4b$
D. $-4x^8y^2$

Lesson 6: Linear Equations and Functions

In this lesson, you will graph linear equations. You can use graphs to identify the slope of a line. You will also investigate functional relationships.

Graphing Linear Equations

To find solutions of a linear equation in two variables, find a pair of numbers, x and y, that make the equation true when the numbers are substituted into it. These values of x and y form an ordered pair (x, y). Use a table of values to generate at least three ordered pairs by choosing any arbitrary value for x or y, substituting that value into the equation, and then solving for the other variable. The easiest values to work with are usually $x = 0$ and $y = 0$.

Example

Find three ordered pairs that are solutions of the following linear equation.

$x + 3y = 6$

Substitute $x = 0$, $y = 0$, and $x = 3$ into the equation to find three ordered pairs.

$(x = 0)$	$(y = 0)$	$(x = 3)$
$x + 3y = 6$	$x + 3y = 6$	$x + 3y = 6$
$\mathbf{0} + 3y = 6$	$x + 3(\mathbf{0}) = 6$	$\mathbf{3} + 3y = 6$
$3y = 6$	$x + 0 = 6$	$3y = 3$
$y = 2$	$x = 6$	$y = 1$

Put these values into a table and find the ordered pairs.

x	y
0	2
6	0
3	1

Three ordered pairs that are solutions of the linear equation $x + 3y = 6$ are $(0, 2)$, $(6, 0)$, and $(3, 1)$.

A linear equation in two variables has an infinite number of solutions. If you were to plot all the solutions on a coordinate plane, they would lie on a straight line. So, when you graph a linear equation, you graph all the points with ordered pairs that are solutions of the linear equation.

Example

Using the ordered pairs you found in the previous example, graph the linear equation $x + 3y = 6$. The ordered pairs are $(0, 2)$, $(6, 0)$, and $(3, 1)$.

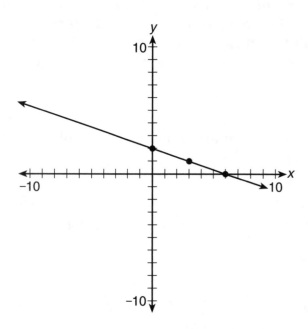

The ordered pairs $(0, 2)$, $(6, 0)$, and $(3, 1)$ are only three solutions of the linear equation $x + 3y = 6$. There is an infinite number of solutions that can be represented by ordered pairs for every point on the line.

In the example, the points $(6, 0)$ and $(0, 2)$ are called the **intercepts** of the graph. The **x-intercept** is the point **$(x, 0)$** where a line crosses (intercepts) the x-axis. Similarly, the **y-intercept** is the point **$(0, y)$** where a line crosses the y-axis.

TIP: It is always a good idea to find at least three ordered pairs to make sure they all lie on a line. If they don't all lie on a line, then at least one ordered pair is incorrect. Check your work.

Practice

Directions: For Numbers 1 through 4, fill in the table with the ordered pairs of the x-intercept, y-intercept, and another point that lie on the graph of the linear equation. Then graph the equation.

1. $2x - y = 4$

x	y

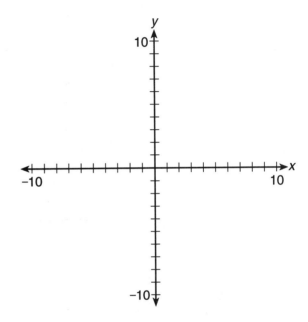

2. $3x + y = 5$

x	y

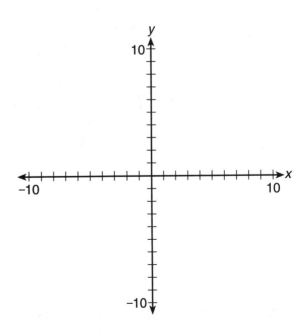

3. $6x - 2y = -4$

x	y

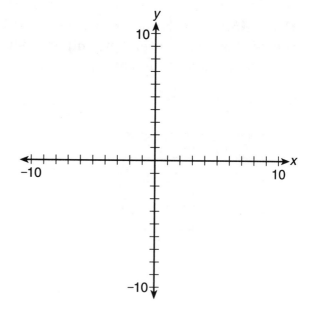

4. $5x + 4y = 20$

x	y

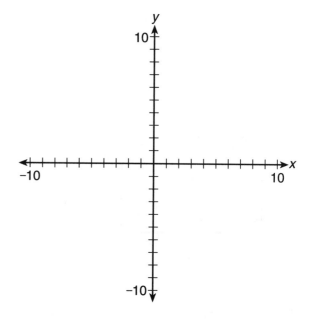

Slope

Slope is the upward or downward slant of a line. A line that slants upward as you follow it from left to right has a **positive** slope. A line that slants downward as you follow it from left to right has a **negative** slope.

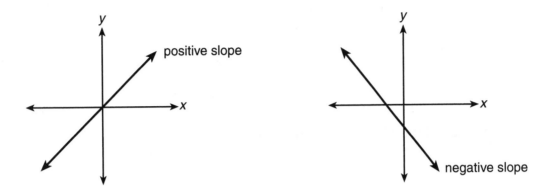

A horizontal line has a **slope of zero**. There is no vertical change in the line as it moves from left to right. A vertical line has an **undefined slope**. There is no horizontal change in the line.

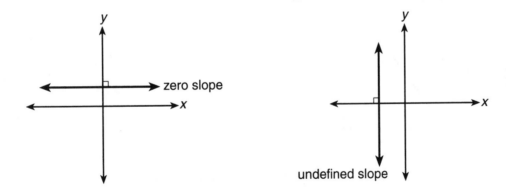

TIP: A horiZontal line has a slope of Zero.

The slope of a line is the ratio of the vertical change of the line to its horizontal change. This is more commonly referred to as $\frac{\text{rise}}{\text{run}}$, or "rise over run." If you know two points on a line, (x_1, y_1) and (x_2, y_2), then the slope of the line can be determined using the following formula:

$$\textbf{slope} = \frac{y_2 - y_1}{x_2 - x_1}$$

Example

Find the slope of the following line.

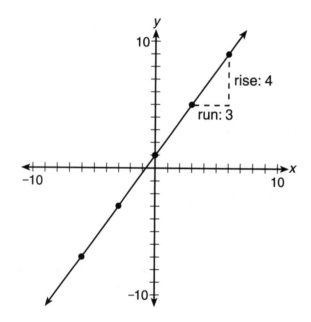

Choose two points on the line to represent (x_1, y_1) and (x_2, y_2).

(x_1, y_1): $(3, 5)$ (x_2, y_2): $(6, 9)$

Substitute the values into the formula to find the slope.

$$\text{slope} = \frac{y_2 - y_1}{x_2 - x_1}$$

$$= \frac{9 - 5}{6 - 3}$$

$$= \frac{4}{3}$$

The slope of the line is $\frac{4}{3}$.

Slope-intercept form

Linear equations can be written in **slope-intercept** form:

$$y = mx + b$$

When written in slope-intercept form, m is the slope of the line, b is the y-intercept, and x and y are the variables. You can plot the y-intercept and then use the slope to graph the linear equation.

Example

Write the following linear equation in slope-intercept form and determine the slope and y-intercept. Then graph the equation.

$$-2x + 3y = 6$$

$$3y = 2x + 6$$

$$y = \frac{2}{3}x + 2$$

slope: $\frac{2}{3}$ **y-intercept:** 2

You can graph the equation by first plotting the y-intercept, $(0, 2)$. Then you use the slope to find the other points. Since the slope is positive, plot another point 2 units up and 3 units to the right of the point $(0, 2)$. You can also plot a point 2 units down and 3 units to the left of $(0, 2)$. The following is the graph of $-2x + 3y = 6$.

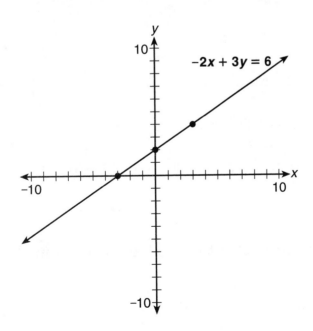

Practice

Directions: For Numbers 1 through 3, find the slope of the line that passes through the given points.

1. (9, 1) and (6, 3)   slope: _____

2. (6, −4) and (4, 6)   slope: _____

3. (3, 2) and (−7, −8)   slope: _____

Directions: Use the following coordinate plane to answer Numbers 4 and 5.

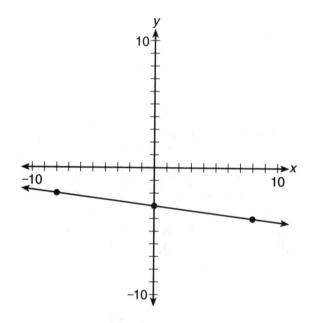

4. Find the slope and y-intercept of the line.

   slope (m): _____ y-intercept (b): _____

5. Write an equation in slope-intercept form to represent the line.

   _____

6. Find the slope and the y-intercept of the graph of the following linear equation.

   $$6x - 3y = -15$$

   slope (m): _____ y-intercept (b): _____

Slopes of parallel lines

Parallel lines lie in the same plane and never intersect. The slopes of parallel lines are equal. The only difference between the equations of parallel lines is their y-intercepts.

Example

What is the slope-intercept form of the line that is parallel to $y = 4x - 3$ and has a y-intercept of 6?

The slope of $y = 4x - 3$ is 4. So, the slope of the line parallel to $y = 4x - 3$ is also 4.

The y-intercept is given as 6.

Substitute the values of the slope and y-intercept into the slope-intercept form.

$$y = mx + b$$
$$y = 4x + 6$$

The slope-intercept form of the line is $y = 4x + 6$.

Practice

1. What is the slope-intercept form of the line that is parallel to $y = -7x + 1$ and has a y-intercept of 9?

   _____

2. What is the slope-intercept form of the line that is parallel to $y = x - \frac{1}{2}$ and has a y-intercept of -5?

   _____

3. What is the slope of a line that is parallel to $-6x + 8y = -7$? _____

4. What is the slope-intercept form of the line that is parallel to $2x - 5y = 2$ and has a y-intercept of -8?

   _____

Functional Relationships

A **function** is a set of ordered pairs (x, y) such that for each value of x, there is one and only one value of y. A set of ordered pairs that includes $(3, 5)$ and $(3, 6)$ does not represent a function, since there are two values of y for one value of x. You can use tables and graphs to show how the change in one variable results in a change in another variable in a functional relationship. A function sometimes uses special notation; instead of y, you might see a function written using $f(x)$. For example, an equation such as $y = x + 5$ may be written as $f(x) = x + 5$ to show that it is a function.

 Example

Does the following equation represent a function?

$y = 3x - 6$

Make a table of ordered pairs and then graph the equation.

x	y
0	−6
1	−3
2	0

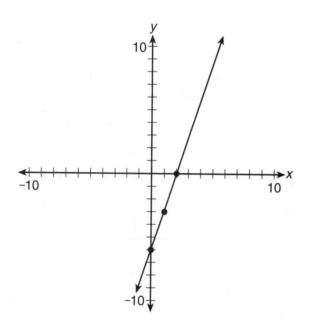

Notice from the table and the graph that for each value of x, there is only one value of y. Therefore, the equation $y = 3x - 6$ represents a function. The equation of the function can be written $f(x) = 3x - 6$ in function notation.

Practice

Directions: For Numbers 1 and 2, complete the table with five ordered pairs that are solutions of the function and then graph the function.

1. $f(x) = \frac{1}{3}x + 1$

x	f(x)

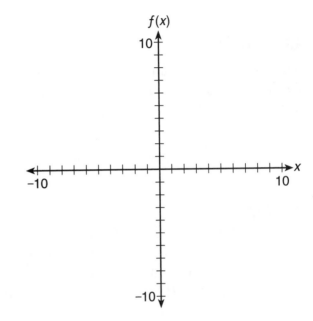

2. $f(x) = -\frac{1}{2}x + 3$

x	f(x)

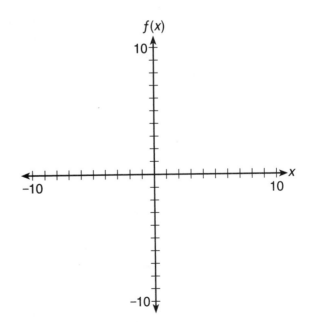

Quantities with Constant Ratios

When you worked with the slope ratio, you found the difference of the *y*-values (rise), the difference of the *x*-values (run), then divided rise by run. No matter which two points along a line you choose, the slope ratio is the same. There are many other real-world situations in which you can plot values on a graph and find that the slope ratio of the values is the same throughout.

Unit price

The **unit price ratio** compares the **total cost** to the **number of items**. You can use the unit price ratio to find the cost per ounce, per bottle, per melon, per carton, per gallon, and so on.

$$\text{unit price} = \frac{\text{total cost}}{\text{number of items}}$$

Example

Paul, Jenn, and Greg went shopping for notebooks together. They all bought the same type of notebook. Paul bought 3 notebooks for $3.75. Jenn bought 5 notebooks for $6.25. Greg bought 8 notebooks for $10. What is the unit price of a notebook?

Find the unit price that Paul, Jenn, and Greg paid for their notebooks.

Paul: unit price $= \dfrac{\text{total cost}}{\text{number of items}} = \dfrac{3.75}{3} = 1.25$

Jenn: unit price $= \dfrac{\text{total cost}}{\text{number of items}} = \dfrac{6.25}{5} = 1.25$

Greg: unit price $= \dfrac{\text{total cost}}{\text{number of items}} = \dfrac{10.00}{8} = 1.25$

The unit price of a notebook is $1.25.

You can take the values from quantities with ratios that are the same, write them as ordered pairs, plot them on a graph, draw a line through them, and find the slope of the line. The slope of the line will be the same as the ratio of the individual values.

Example

Use the information from the example on page 108 to write ordered pairs for the purchases (number of items, total cost), plot them on a graph, draw a line through the points, and find the slope of the line.

The ordered pairs are: (3, 3.75), (5, 6.25), and (8, 10).

Plot the ordered pairs on a graph. Then draw a line through the points.

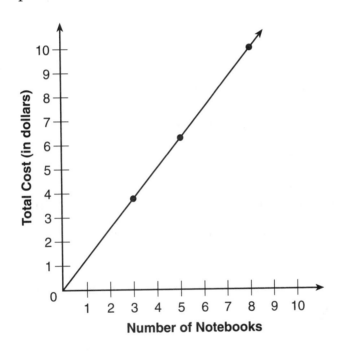

Take any two points from the graph and find the slope of the line that was drawn through the points.

$$\text{slope} = \frac{y_2 - y_1}{x_2 - x_1} = \frac{6.25 - 3.75}{5 - 3} = \frac{2.5}{2} = 1.25$$

Notice that the slope of the line drawn through the points is equal to the unit price of a notebook.

Other constant ratios

Constant ratios are used frequently to convert different units of measurement.

Example

The following graph shows the relationship between feet and yards.

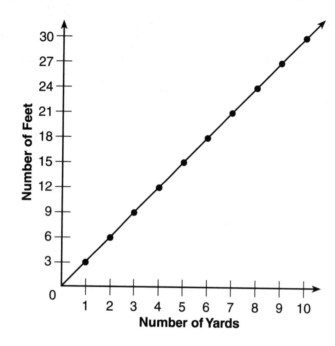

Take any two points from the graph and find the slope of the line.

$$\text{slope} = \frac{y_2 - y_1}{x_2 - x_1} = \frac{9 - 18}{3 - 6} = \frac{-9}{-3} = 3$$

Notice that the slope of the line is equal to the ratio used to convert feet to yards: $\frac{3 \text{ ft}}{1 \text{ yd}}$.

Example

The following table of values shows the relationship between the circumference and the diameter of a circle.

Diameter (d)	Circumference (C)
1	3.14
2	6.28
3	9.42
4	12.56
5	15.70
6	18.84

Put the ordered pairs from the table on a graph. Then draw the line through the points.

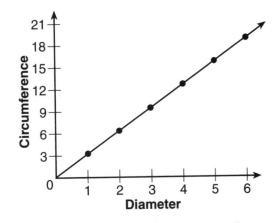

The constant ratio is $\frac{\text{circumference}}{\text{diameter}}$. What is the slope of the line? When you select any two points and calculate the value of the slope, you'll get 3.14 each time. This is the approximate value of π. In summary, this graph shows that $\pi = \frac{C}{d}$.

Take any two points from the table or graph and find the slope of the line.

$$\text{slope} = \frac{y_2 - y_1}{x_2 - x_1} = \frac{12.56 - 6.28}{4 - 2} = \frac{6.28}{2} = 3.14$$

Notice that the slope of the line is equal to 3.14, the approximate value of π.

Practice

Directions: Use the following information to answer Numbers 1 through 3.

This table of values shows how computer memory is related.

Number of Bytes	Number of Bits
1	8
2	16
3	24
4	32
5	40

1. Plot the points from the table on the following graph and draw a line through the points.

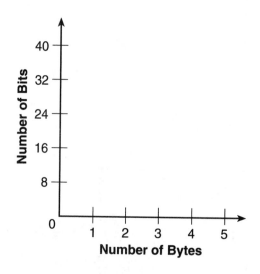

2. What is the slope of the line from the graph? Show your work.

    slope: _____

3. What is the bits per byte ratio? _____

4. A recipe for 3 dozen cookies calls for 2 cups of flour. Eric increased the recipe to make 126 cookies. He used 7 cups of flour. Did he use the correct amount of flour to make the 126 cookies? Explain.

_____

_____

_____

Directions: Use the following information to answer Numbers 5 and 6.

Chef Harvey needs to refill his sugar supply. He called the distributor who sells him sugar. Pure white cane sugar would cost him $2.50 for each 10-pound bag, $4.40 for each 20-pound bag, and $4.50 for each 30-pound bag.

5. Plot the values on the following graph.

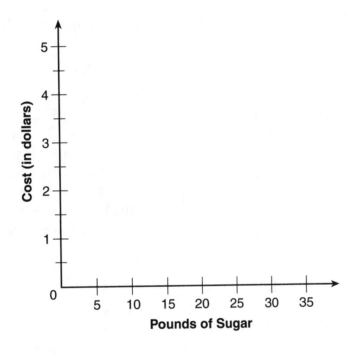

6. Why are you unable to draw a straight line through the values?

_____

_____

_____

Test Your Skills

1. What is the slope-intercept form of the following graph?

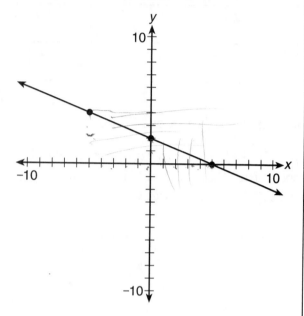

    A. $y = \frac{2}{5}x + 2$

    B. $y = \frac{2}{5}x - 2$

    C. $y = -\frac{2}{5}x - 2$

    D. $y = -\frac{2}{5}x + 2$

2. Cara baby-sat for the McDonalds last Friday for 4 hours and made $18. She baby-sat for the Battles last Saturday for 3 hours. Her hourly rate is always the same. How much did the Battles pay Cara?

    A. $4.50
    B. $9.00
    C. $12.00
    D. $13.50

3. Which ordered pair represents the *y*-intercept of the following line?

$$5x + 2y = 10$$

    A. (0, −5)
    B. (0, −2)
    C. (0, 5)
    D. (0, 2)

4. Which point lies on the following line?

$$12x - y = 8$$

    A. (−8, 0)
    B. (2, 16)
    C. (0, 8)
    D. (4, 1)

5. The slope of a line is 2. If the vertical change between two points that lie on the line is 8, what is the horizontal change between the two points?

    A. 16
    B. 4
    C. 2
    D. 1

6. What is the slope of a line parallel to the following line?

$$4x - y = -12$$

    A. 4
    B. 3
    C. −3
    D. −4

7. Which graph represents
   $2x + y = -3$?

   A.

   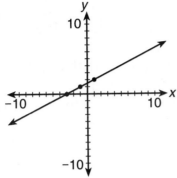

   B.

   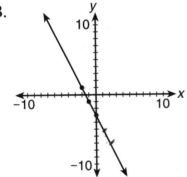

   C.

   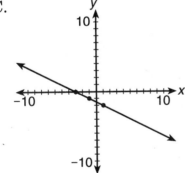

   D.

   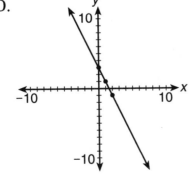

8. Which graph shows the
   relationship between days
   and weeks?

   A.

   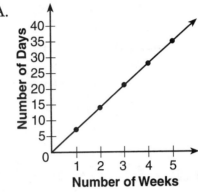

   B.

   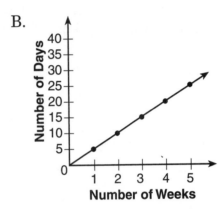

   C.

   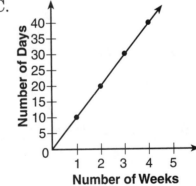

   D.

   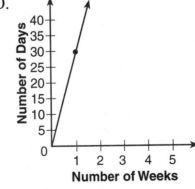

Lesson 7: Systems of Linear Equations

A **system of linear equations** consists of two or more linear equations. A solution to a system of linear equations is an ordered pair that makes all the equations in the system true. There are three types of systems of linear equations, each with a different number of solutions. A **consistent** system will have **one solution**. An **inconsistent** system will have **no solution**. A **dependent** system will have an **infinite number of solutions**. There are three ways to solve a system of linear equations: graphically, using substitution, or using linear combinations.

Solving Systems of Equations Graphically

To solve a system of linear equations graphically, graph each linear equation on the same coordinate plane. The solution(s) will be the ordered pair(s) of the point(s) where all of the graphs intersect. The slope and y-intercept of the graph of each equation will determine the type of system.

Consistent system

- exactly one solution
- different slopes

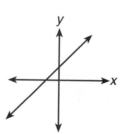

Inconsistent system

- no solution
- same slopes, different y-intercepts

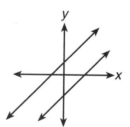

Dependent system

- infinite number of solutions
- same slopes, same y-intercepts

Solving Systems of Linear Equations Using Substitution

When you use graphing to solve a system of linear equations, you may have difficulty locating the exact point of intersection. Another way of solving a system of linear equations is to use substitution.

Example

Solve the following system of linear equations using substitution.

$$5x - 4y = 15$$
$$x + y = 3$$

Step 1: **Solve one of the equations for one of the variables.** In this case, solve the second equation for y.

$$x + y = 3$$
$$y = 3 - x$$

Step 2: **Substitute the expression for the variable from Step 1 into the other equation and solve for the remaining variable.** Substitute $3 - x$ for y in the first equation and solve.

$$5x - 4y = 15$$
$$5x - 4(\mathbf{3 - x}) = 15$$
$$5x - 12 + 4x = 15$$
$$9x = 27$$
$$\mathbf{x = 3}$$

Step 3: **Substitute the value for the variable into one of the original equations and solve for the remaining variable.** Substitute 3 for x in the second equation and solve.

$$x + y = 3$$
$$\mathbf{3} + y = 3$$
$$\mathbf{y = 0}$$

Step 4: **Check the values in the original equations.**

$$\textbf{Check (3, 0): } 5x - 4y = 15 \qquad\qquad x + y = 3$$
$$5(3) - 4(0) = 15 \qquad\qquad \mathbf{3 + 0} = 3$$
$$15 - 0 = 15 \qquad\qquad 3 = 3 \quad \textbf{true}$$
$$15 = 15 \quad \textbf{true}$$

Since the ordered pair makes both equations true, this is a consistent system of linear functions. The solution is (3, 0).

Sometimes, after you substitute for the first variable and simplify (Step 2), the remaining variable term will disappear. In this case, there are no variables remaining. This will be the case if the system is inconsistent or dependent.

If the equation that is left is false, the system is inconsistent and has no solution (the graphs will be parallel).

Example

After Step 2 from page 117, you may have an equation similar to this one remaining.

$$0 = 21$$

Since the equation is false, this is an inconsistent system of linear functions. There is no solution.

If the equation that is left is true, the system is dependent and has an infinite number of solutions. The solutions will be all the ordered pairs of all the points on the graph of either function (the graphs will be the same).

Example

After Step 2 from page 117, you may have an equation similar to this one remaining.

$$0 = 0$$

Since the equation is true, this is a dependent system of linear functions. There are an infinite number of solutions. The solutions are all the ordered pairs that make either equation in the system true.

Solving Systems of Equations Using Linear Combinations

The third way of solving a system of linear equations is to use **linear combinations**. To solve a system of linear equations using linear combinations, multiply one or both equations by a constant factor, when necessary, so that the coefficients of either x or y are additive inverses (opposites). Then, add the equations to get an equation in one variable. Next, solve for the variable and substitute that value into one of the original equations and solve for the remaining variable. Finally, check to be sure the values make both equations true. In using this method, it is easier if both equations are written in **standard form:** $Ax + By = C$.

Example

Solve the following system of linear equations using linear combinations.

$$x + y = 5$$
$$x - y = 9$$

The equations are already in standard form and the coefficients of y are already additive inverses (1 and −1). If you add the equations as they appear, the y-term will drop out.

$$x + y = 5$$
$$\underline{x - y = 9}$$
$$2x = 14 \quad \text{(The y-term dropped out; the x-term remains.)}$$
$$x = 7$$

Substitute $x = 7$ into either original equation and solve.

$$x + y = 5$$
$$7 + y = 5$$
$$y = -2$$

The solution looks as if it is the ordered pair (7, −2). Check the solution (7, −2) by making sure the values make both equations true.

$x + y = 5$	$x - y = 9$
$7 + (-2) = 5$	$7 - (-2) = 9$
$5 = 5$ **true**	$9 = 9$ **true**

This is a consistent system. The solution is (7, −2).

Here is an example in which you need to multiply each equation by a constant factor before you add them.

Example

Solve the following system of linear equations using linear combinations.

$$5x + 3y = -9$$
$$2x - 5y = -16$$

Multiply the first equation by 5 and the second equation by 3 to get the additive inverses of 15 and -15 as coefficients of y, then add. In this case, it may be easier to eliminate y than x because the signs of the y-terms are already opposites.

$$5(5x + 3y = -9) \longrightarrow 25x + 15y = -45$$
$$3(2x - 5y = -16) \longrightarrow \underline{6x - 15y = -48}$$
$$31x = -93$$
$$\boldsymbol{x = -3}$$

Substitute $x = -3$ into either original equation and solve. It is important to use one of the original equations since there may have been a multiplication error made in creating the additive inverses. In this example, use the first equation, which shows a positive y-term (this avoids division by a negative and may make your work easier).

$$5(\boldsymbol{-3}) + 3y = -9$$
$$-15 + 3y = -9$$
$$3y = 6$$
$$\boldsymbol{y = 2}$$

Check the solution $(-3, 2)$ by making sure the values make both equations true.

$$5(\boldsymbol{-3}) + 3(\boldsymbol{2}) = -9 \qquad\qquad 2(\boldsymbol{-3}) - 5(\boldsymbol{2}) = -16$$
$$-15 + 6 = -9 \qquad\qquad -6 - 10 = -16$$
$$-9 = -9 \textbf{ true} \qquad\qquad -16 = -16 \textbf{ true}$$

This is a consistent system. The solution is $(-3, 2)$.

Just as with substitution, sometimes both variable terms will drop out when you add the equations. At that point, determine whether the resulting equation is true or false.

If the equation that is left is false, the system is inconsistent and has no solution (the graphs will be parallel).

If the equation that is left is true, the system is dependent and has an infinite number of solutions. The solutions are all the ordered pairs that make either equation in the system true (the graphs will be the same).

Practice

Directions: For Numbers 1 through 8, solve the systems of linear equations using either substitution or linear combinations.

1. $3x + y = 20$
   $4x - y = 8$

   solution(s): _____

   _____

   The system is _____.

2. $3x + 4y = 7$
   $6x + 8y = 14$

   solution(s): _____

   _____

   The system is _____.

3. $3x + 5y = 28$
   $5x - 3y = 24$

   solution(s): _____

   _____

   The system is _____.

4. $5x - 7y = -16$
   $2x + 8y = 26$

solution(s): _____

_____

The system is _____.

5. $3x - y = 2$
   $6x - 2y = 3$

solution(s): _____

_____

The system is _____.

6. $9x - 8y = -4$
   $4x + 3y = 31$

solution(s): _____

_____

The system is _____.

7. $3x + y = 2$
   $x + 2y = 4$

solution(s): _____

_____

The system is _____.

8. $-3x + 5y = 15$
   $2x - 4y = -13$

solution(s): _____

_____

The system is _____.

Systems of linear equations applications

There are many real-world situations that can be represented by a system of linear equations.

 Example

A company has fixed costs of $3,600 and variable costs of $2.25 per disk to produce computer disks. The disks sell for $4.50 each. How many disks must be produced and sold for the total cost to equal the revenue generated by the sales? At what dollar amount are the total cost and the revenue the same?

Set up the system of linear equations that represents the information. Let x = number of disks and y = number of dollars.

$y = 2.25x + 3,600$ (total cost of production)
$y = 4.50x$ (revenue generated by sales)

Use substitution or linear combinations to solve the system of linear equations. Since the equations are already solved for y, use substitution. Substitute $4.50x$ for y in the first equation and solve for x.

$$y = 2.25x + 3,600$$

$$\mathbf{4.50x} = 2.25x + 3,600$$

$$2.25x = 3,600$$

$$x = 1,600$$

Now solve for y.

$$y = 4.50x$$

$$y = 4.50 \cdot 1,600$$

$$y = 7,200$$

The solution of the system appears to be (1,600, 7,200).

Check (1,600, 7,200) by verifying that the values make both equations true.

$y = 2.25x + 3,600$ $y = 4.50x$

$\mathbf{7,200} = 2.25 \cdot \mathbf{1,600} + 3,600$ $\mathbf{7,200} = 4.50 \cdot \mathbf{1,600}$

$7,200 = 7,200$ **true** $7,200 = 7,200$ **true**

The following is the graph of this system of linear equations. Since the number of disks produced and the dollar amounts must be positive or zero, only the first quadrant is shown in the graph.

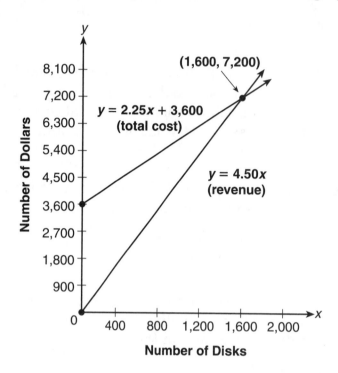

The number of disks that must be produced and sold for the total cost to equal the revenue is 1,600. The dollar amount at which the total cost equals the revenue is $7,200. This information is given by the point of intersection (1,600, 7,200).

The graph shows that the revenue generated by the sales of the disks is growing faster than the cost of producing the disks. The slope of the revenue line (4.50) is greater than the slope of the cost line (2.25). For any number of disks greater than 1,600, the revenue is greater than the total cost. Therefore, the company starts to profit after 1,600 disks are sold.

Practice

Directions: For Numbers 1 and 2, set up a system of linear equations to represent each situation. Then use either substitution or linear combinations to solve the system of linear equations and answer the questions.

1. There were a total of 480 tickets sold for the school play. Adult tickets sold for $8 and student tickets sold for $5. The ticket sales brought in $3,369. How many adult tickets, a, and student tickets, s, were sold? Write your answer as (a, s).

2. Mr. Kotter and Mr. Belding each ordered school supplies from the same company. Mr. Kotter ordered 6 boxes of dry erase markers and 4 boxes of overhead markers for $50. Mr. Belding ordered 8 boxes of the dry erase markers and 3 boxes of the overhead markers for $56.75. What was the price of a box of dry erase markers, d? What was the price of a box of overhead markers, m?

Test Your Skills

1. What is the solution of the following system of linear equations?

$$3x - 8y = 4$$
$$x - 4y = 2$$

A. $\left(0, -\frac{1}{2}\right)$

B. $(-2, 0)$

C. There is no solution.

D. There are an infinite number of solutions.

2. Determine the solution of the system of linear equations from the following graph.

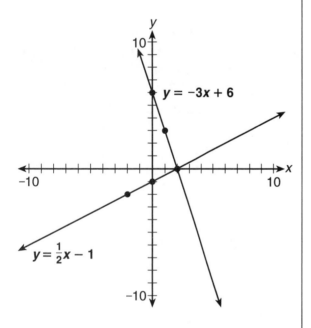

A. $(1, 3)$

B. $(2, 0)$

C. $(3, 1)$

D. $(0, 2)$

3. Which system of linear functions represents the following information?

Freddie bought 5 CDs for $63. Each CD costs either $11 or $15. How many CDs did Freddie buy that cost $11?

A. $11x + y = 5$
   $x + 15y = 63$

B. $x + y = 63$
   $11x + 15y = 5$

C. $x + y = 5$
   $11x + 15y = 63$

D. $x + 11y = 5$
   $15x + y = 63$

4. What is the solution of the following system of linear equations?

$$2x + y = 8$$
$$4x - 5y = 2$$

A. $(4, 4)$

B. $(2, 5)$

C. $(3, 2)$

D. $(-2, 2)$

Lesson 8: Quadratic and Cubic Functions

In this lesson, you will learn how to graph and interpret two types of nonlinear functions.

Quadratic Functions

The graph of a **quadratic function** is called a **parabola** (a U-shaped curve). The equation used to graph a parabola is in the form $f(x) = nx^2$. In this lesson, n will be any rational number except zero. Here are some examples of quadratic functions:

$$f(x) = 3x^2 \qquad f(x) = -\frac{1}{2}x^2 \qquad f(x) = -x^2 \qquad f(x) = 2.5x^2$$

You can graph a quadratic function by using a table of values. The parabola will open upward if the squared term has a positive coefficient, and it will open downward if the squared term has a negative coefficient. (Some parabolas will open to the left or to the right, but they are not functions.)

 Example

Graph the quadratic function $f(x) = -\frac{1}{2}x^2$.

The x-values you choose will affect the resulting $f(x)$-values. For example, you can avoid fractional values of $f(x)$ by selecting only even values of x. Since that seems like a good idea, here is a table of values that consists of only even values of x.

x	f(x)
–4	–8
–2	–2
0	0
2	–2
4	–8

Now use the table of values to graph the function.

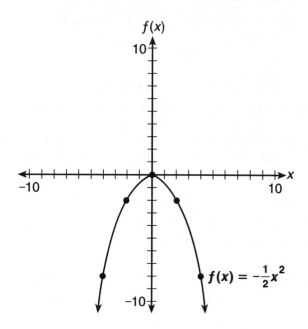

$$f(x) = -\frac{1}{2}x^2$$

A parabola will fold over onto itself. Once you have found the "turn-around" point, called the **vertex**, all you need to do is find the "mirror images" of the other points that have been plotted.

In the previous example, the vertex is located at (0, 0). You can see the vertex on the graph, but you can also find it in the table of values. The $f(x)$-values "turn around" and repeat themselves in the reverse order at 0. Notice that (−4, −8) and (4, −8), as well as (−2, −2) and (2, −2), are "mirror images" of each other.

TIP: Remember that $f(x)$ is function notation for y. The phrase "$f(x)$-values" refers to y-values. Remember to plot them on the vertical axis.

Parabolas can show up in application problems. The following example provides a look at the application of a quadratic function.

Example

The great Italian scientist Galileo performed many experiments to calculate how quickly objects of different masses fall (discounting air resistance). He concluded that distance in feet, $f(t)$, is a function of time in seconds, t. He also concluded that his formula $f(t) = 16t^2$ was correct.

During one alleged experiment, Galileo dropped a rock from the top of a tower in Pisa. He noted that it hit the ground in 4 seconds. How high is the point from which Galileo dropped the rock?

Substitute $t = 4$ into the formula: $f(t) = 16t^2$

$$f(t) = 16(4)^2$$

$$f(t) = 16(16)$$

$$f(t) = 256$$

Galileo dropped the rock from a height of 256 feet.

If you make a table of values for this quadratic function, what type of values will be omitted? Since time and distance cannot be negative, you'll use only whole numbers. The graph will look like this:

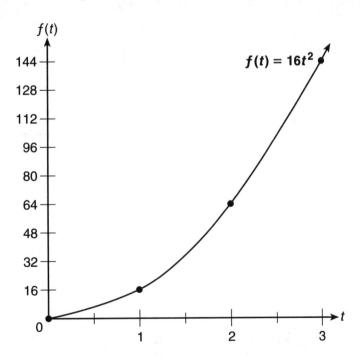

Practice

1. Leonardo da Vinci showed how a mirror shaped like a parabola was used to produce a beam of light. He based his observation on the quadratic function $f(x) = x^2$. Complete the following table of values for the function. Then graph the function.

x	f(x)
−4	
−3	
−2	
−1	
0	
1	
2	
3	
4	

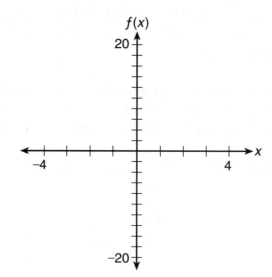

2. Complete the following table of values for the quadratic function $f(x) = x^2 + 2$. Then graph the function.

x	f(x)
−4	
−3	
−2	
−1	
0	
1	
2	
3	
4	

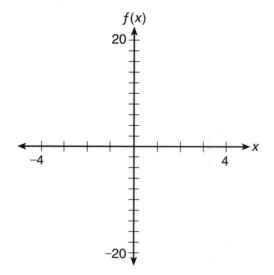

3. Make your own table of values for the quadratic function $f(x) = -2x^2$. Then graph the function.

x	f(x)

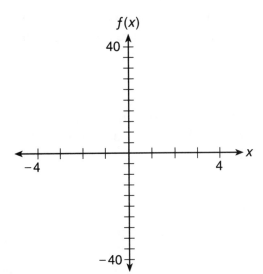

4. The cables of a suspension bridge form a parabola when the weight of the bridge is attached. The Golden Gate Bridge in San Francisco has this type of cable. Here is a formula that approximates the curve of the cables: $f(x) = 5x^2 - 100x + 700$. Complete the following table of values for the function. Then graph the function.

x	f(x)
0	
2	
4	
6	
8	
10	
12	

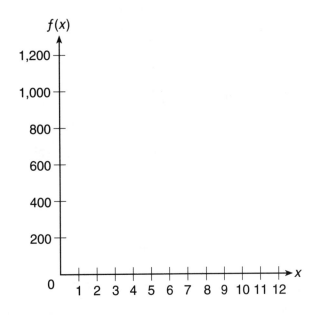

5. Brooke and Ridge were sitting on a bridge, dangling their feet over the side. After a few minutes, Brooke's sandal slid off her foot and dropped into the water. It took the sandal three seconds to hit the water. Assuming there was no resistance, what is the approximate height of the bridge? Use $f(t) = 16t^2$.

Cubic Functions

Functions in the form $f(x) = nx^3$ are called **cubic functions** (the variable x is cubed, or raised to the third power). In this lesson, n will be any rational number except zero. Here are some examples of cubic functions:

$$f(x) = x^3 \qquad f(x) = -\frac{1}{2}x^3 \qquad f(x) = -x^3 \qquad f(x) = 2.5x^3$$

You can graph a cubic function by using a table of values. When you choose negative numbers for x-values, remember that the cube of a negative number is also negative.

 Example

Graph the cubic function $f(x) = x^3$.

If you choose both positive and negative x-values, you will see a more accurate picture of the function.

x	$f(x)$
−3	−27
−2	−8
−1	−1
0	0
1	1
2	8
3	27

Now use the table of values to graph the function.

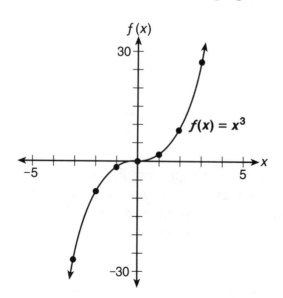

Practice

1. Make a table of values for the cubic function $f(x) = 2x^3$. Then graph the function.

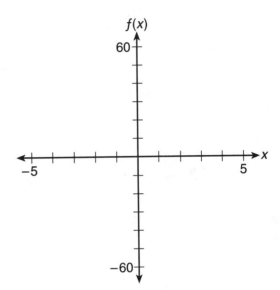

2. Make a table of values for the cubic function $f(x) = -\frac{1}{2}x^3$. Then graph the function.

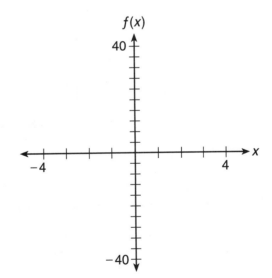

Directions: Use the following information to answer Numbers 3 through 5.

Windmills can be used to generate electrical power. The power generated by a windmill is a function of the wind speed. Here is one formula for this function: $f(s) = \left(\frac{s}{10}\right)^3$, where $f(s)$ is the power generated and s is the wind speed in kilometers per hour.

3. Complete the following table of values for the function. Then graph the function.

s	f(s)
0	
10	
20	
30	
40	
50	

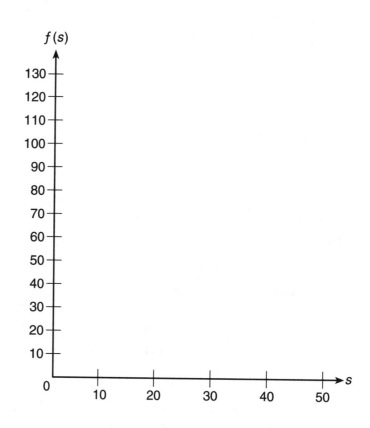

4. Why aren't there any negative values of s in the table?

_____

5. What happens to power generated by the windmill when the wind speed triples?

_____

Test Your Skills

1. Which function does the following graph represent?

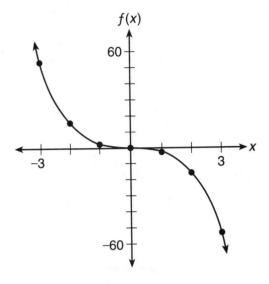

A. $f(x) = 2x^2$

B. $f(x) = 2x^3$

C. $f(x) = -2x^2$

D. $f(x) = -2x^3$

2. Jordan's dad has 40 feet of fencing to build a rectangular dog kennel. The back of the garage will serve as one side of the kennel. The area of the kennel can be found by the function $f(x) = 40x - 2x^2$, where $f(x)$ is the area of the kennel and x is how far the kennel extends from the garage. What is the area in ft² of the kennel if the kennel extends 10 feet from the garage?

A. 200 ft²

B. 250 ft²

C. 300 ft²

D. 350 ft²

3. A rocket is launched straight up at an initial velocity of 80 ft/s. The height of the rocket can be found using the function $f(t) = 80t - 16t^2$, where $f(t)$ is the height of the rocket and t is the time in seconds after the launch. This is the graph of the function.

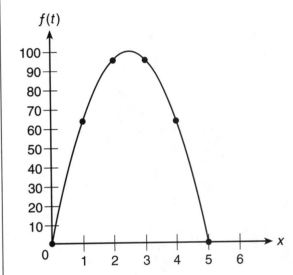

According to the graph, when is the rocket at a height of 84 feet?

A. 0.5 and 4.5 seconds

B. 1 and 4 seconds

C. 1.5 and 3.5 seconds

D. 2 and 3 seconds

4. Which is the graph of the function $f(x) = 5x^2$?

A.

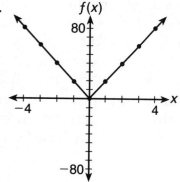

B.

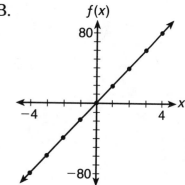

C.

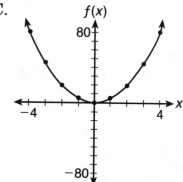

D.

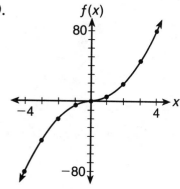

5. Which is the graph of the function $f(x) = x^3$?

A.

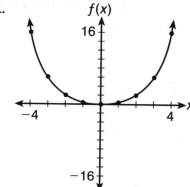

B.

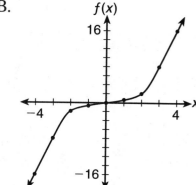

C.

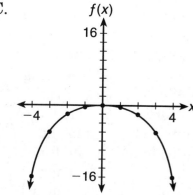

D.

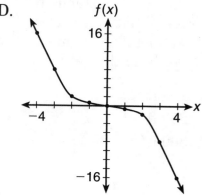

Unit 3

Measurement and Geometry

Have you ever tried to put up a poster so that it hangs perfectly straight on the wall? Have you ever figured out how many two-liter bottles of soda you would need to serve a group of friends or classmates? Or maybe you've had to figure out the number of gallons of paint needed to paint a room. These skills require the use of measurement and geometry concepts.

In this unit, you will use conversion ratios to convert within and between the metric and U.S. customary systems. You will review the definitions and qualities of two- and three-dimensional figures. You will find area, perimeter, circumference, surface area, and volume. You will find missing side lengths of right triangles, find congruent corresponding side lengths or angle measurements, and draw transformations, including translations, rotations, and reflections.

In This Unit

Measurement

Geometric Measurement

Geometric Concepts

Lesson 9: Measurement

In this lesson, you will use ratios to convert to the appropriate unit within and between the metric and U.S. customary measurement systems. You will also solve problems using the correct units.

Measurement Systems

The values of the metric units are based on powers of 10. When you measure with metric units, use the following table of prefixes to help you.

kilo	hecto	deka	deci	centi	milli
thousands	hundreds	tens	ten**ths**	hundred**ths**	thousand**ths**

The values of the U.S. customary units vary.

Length

The following tables show units of length ordered from smallest unit to largest unit. They also show the conversion relationships between units of the same system.

Metric	Conversion
millimeter (mm) about the thickness of a paper match	$1 \text{ mm} = \frac{1}{10} \text{ cm}$
centimeter (cm) about the radius of a nickel	1 cm = 10 mm
meter (m) about the height of a kitchen table	1 m = 100 cm
kilometer (km) about 6 city blocks	1 km = 1,000 m

U.S. Customary	Conversion
inch (in.) about the diameter of a quarter	$1 \text{ in.} = \frac{1}{12} \text{ ft}$
foot (ft) about the length of a spaghetti noodle	1 ft = 12 in.
yard (yd) about the length of a baseball bat	1 yd = 3 ft 1 yd = 36 in.
mile (mi) about 10 city blocks	1 mi = 1,760 yd 1 mi = 5,280 ft

Weight

The following tables show units of weight ordered from smallest unit to largest unit. They also show the conversion relationships between units of the same system.

Metric	Conversion
milligram (mg) about the weight of the wing of a housefly	$1 \text{ mg} = \frac{1}{1,000} \text{ g}$
gram (g) about the weight of a paper clip	$1 \text{ g} = 1,000 \text{ mg}$
kilogram (kg) about the weight of one volume of an encyclopedia	$1 \text{ kg} = 1,000 \text{ g}$

U.S. Customary	Conversion
ounce (oz) about the weight of a slice of bread	$1 \text{ oz} = \frac{1}{16} \text{ lb}$
pound (lb) about the weight of a full can of soda	$1 \text{ lb} = 16 \text{ oz}$
ton (T) about the weight of a small car	$1 \text{ T} = 2,000 \text{ lb}$

Capacity

The following tables show units of capacity ordered from smallest unit to largest unit. They also show the conversion relationships between units of the same system.

Metric	Conversion
milliliter (mL) about what an eyedropper holds	$1 \text{ mL} = \frac{1}{1,000} \text{ L}$
liter (L) about what a medium plastic soda bottle holds	$1 \text{ L} = 1,000 \text{ mL}$
kiloliter (kL) about what a large wading pool holds	$1 \text{ kL} = 1,000 \text{ L}$

U.S. Customary	Conversion
teaspoon (tsp)	$1 \text{ tsp} = \frac{1}{3} \text{ tbsp}$
tablespoon (tbsp)	$1 \text{ tbsp} = 3 \text{ tsp}$
fluid ounce (fl oz)	$1 \text{ fl oz} = 2 \text{ tbsp}$
cup (c)	$1 \text{ c} = 8 \text{ fl oz}$
pint (pt)	$1 \text{ pt} = 2 \text{ c}$
quart (qt)	$1 \text{ qt} = 2 \text{ pt}$ $1 \text{ qt} = 4 \text{ c}$
gallon (gal)	$1 \text{ gal} = 4 \text{ qt}$ $1 \text{ gal} = 8 \text{ pt}$ $1 \text{ gal} = 16 \text{ c}$

Conversions between systems

The following table shows the conversion relationships between units of different systems.

	Metric to U.S. Customary	**U.S. Customary to Metric**
Length	1 cm ≈ 0.3937 in. 1 m ≈ 1.094 yd 1 km ≈ 0.6214 mi	1 in. ≈ 2.540 cm 1 yd ≈ 0.9144 m 1 mi ≈ 1.609 km
Weight	1 g ≈ 0.03529 oz 1 kg ≈ 2.205 lb	1 oz ≈ 28.34 g 1 lb ≈ 0.4535 kg
Capacity	1 mL ≈ 0.03381 fl oz 1 L ≈ 1.057 qt	1 fl oz ≈ 29.58 mL 1 qt ≈ 0.9461 L

Time

The units of time are the same in both systems. The following table shows the conversion relationships between the units.

Unit	Conversion
seconds (s)	$1 \text{ s} = \frac{1}{60} \text{ min}$
minutes (min)	1 min = 60 s
hour (hr)	1 hr = 60 min
day (d)	1 d = 24 hr

Unit	Conversion
week (wk)	1 wk = 7 d
month (mo)	1 mo ≈ 4 wk
year (yr)	1 yr = 12 mo 1 yr = 52 wk 1 yr = 365–366 d

Temperature

Temperature uses two different units. The following table shows units of temperature.

System	Unit	Water freezes at . . .	Water boils at . . .
Metric	Celsius (C)	0 C	100 C
U.S. Customary	Fahrenheit (F)	32 F	212 F

There is no simple equation that shows the conversion relationship between temperature units. Instead, the following formulas are needed.

To convert from degrees Celsius to degrees Fahrenheit, use the following formula.

$$°F = \left(\frac{9}{5} \cdot °C\right) + 32$$

To convert from degrees Fahrenheit to degrees Celsius, use the following formula.

$$°C = \frac{5}{9}(°F - 32)$$

Example

The average temperature in March in Berlin, Germany, is 3.5°C. What is Berlin's average March temperature in °F?

Since you are converting from °C to °F, use

$$°F = \left(\frac{9}{5} \cdot °C\right) + 32$$

Substitute 3.5 for °C and simplify.

$$°F = \left(\frac{9}{5} \cdot 3.5\right) + 32$$

$$= 6.3 + 32$$

$$= 38.3$$

Berlin's average March temperature is 38.3°F.

Conversions Within and Between Measurement Systems

You can use the conversion factors that were listed in the tables on pages 138 through 140 to convert within and between measurement systems. To do so, write the conversion between the units as a ratio and multiply this ratio by the original amount. The key part of this process is to set up the ratio in such a way that the unit you are **converting to** is in the **numerator** and the unit you are **converting from** is in the **denominator**. This is called **dimensional analysis**. That way, the old unit will divide out and the new unit will remain.

Example

How many quarts is 8 L? Round your answer to the nearest hundredth.

Write the conversion from L to qt as a ratio.

$1 \text{ L} \approx 1.057 \text{ qt}: \frac{1.057 \text{ qt}}{1 \text{ L}}$ 　　　　$1 \text{ qt} \approx 0.9461 \text{ L}: \frac{1 \text{ qt}}{0.9461 \text{ L}}$

Multiply the original amount (8 L) by this ratio.

$8 \cancel{\text{L}} \cdot \frac{1.057 \text{ qt}}{1 \cancel{\text{L}}} = 8.46 \text{ qt}$ 　　　　$8 \cancel{\text{L}} \cdot \frac{1 \text{ qt}}{0.9461 \cancel{\text{L}}} = 8.46 \text{ qt}$

8 L is about 8.46 qt.

Sometimes you will need to convert a rate to different units. This may involve more than one conversion ratio.

Example

A car is traveling at the speed of 80 km/hr. What is the car's speed in meters per minute (m/min)? Round your answer to the nearest hundredth.

Write the conversions from km to m and hr to min as ratios.

$1 \text{ km} = 1,000 \text{ m}: \frac{1,000 \text{ m}}{1 \text{ km}}$ 　　　　$1 \text{ hr} = 60 \text{ min}: \frac{1 \text{ hr}}{60 \text{ min}}$

Multiply the original amount $\left(\frac{80 \text{ km}}{1 \text{ hr}} \right)$ by these ratios.

$\frac{80 \cancel{\text{km}}}{1 \cancel{\text{hr}}} \cdot \frac{1,000 \text{ m}}{1 \cancel{\text{km}}} \cdot \frac{1 \cancel{\text{hr}}}{60 \text{ min}} = 1,333.33 \text{ m/min}$

The car's speed is about 1,333.33 m/min.

 TIP: You may need to convert a couple of times if there is no direct conversion ratio between units.

Practice

Directions: For Numbers 1 through 8, convert the measurement to the given unit or rate. Round your answers to the nearest hundredth when necessary.

1. 5 gal = _____ pt

2. 48 oz = _____ lb

3. 16 km = _____ m

4. 5.75 kg = _____ g

5. 5 yd ≈ _____ m

6. 10°C = _____ °F

7. 60 fl oz/min ≈ _____ mL/s

8. 18,000 km/hr ≈ _____ mi/s

9. The density of aluminum is 2.70 g/mL. What is the approximate density of aluminum in oz/mL?

_____ oz/mL

10. A gray fox can reach a top running speed of 42 mi/hr. What is the gray fox's top running speed in ft/s?

_____ ft/s

11. Gene can type an average of 75 words per minute. What is Gene's average rate of words typed per hour?

A. 3,600 words per hour
B. 4,050 words per hour
C. 4,500 words per hour
D. 4,950 words per hour

12. Shrimp is on sale for $12.50/kg. What is the sale price of the shrimp in ¢/g?

A. 1.25¢/g
B. 2.50¢/g
C. 125¢/g
D. 250¢/g

Problem solving with units

Rates can be used to solve problems. The rates can act as the conversion ratio. Use dimensional analysis to eliminate the proper unit.

Example

Pat is running a marathon that is 26.2 miles. He ran the first mile in 8 minutes and plans to continue at the same pace for the rest of the marathon. How long will it take Pat to finish the marathon in minutes? in hours?

You need to multiply 26.2 by the rate at which Pat is running. Use dimensional analysis to write the rate so that the miles will divide out.

$$26.2 \text{ mi} \cdot \frac{8 \text{ min}}{1 \text{ mi}} = 209.6 \text{ min}$$

Convert the minutes to hours.

$$209.6 \text{ min} \cdot \frac{1 \text{ hr}}{60 \text{ min}} = 3.49\overline{3} \text{ hr}$$

It will take Pat 209.6 minutes or $3.49\overline{3}$ hours to finish the marathon.

Sometimes the units of a solution are in the form of a product (kilowatt-hours, person-days) instead of a ratio (miles per hour, feet per second). This tells you to multiply to find the solution.

Example

Shelly's microwave uses an average of 1.45 kilowatts of energy. She used her microwave for 5 hours last month. How many kilowatt-hours of energy did Shelly's microwave use last month?

The problem asks you to find the number of kilowatt-hours. To do this, multiply the kilowatts the microwave uses and the hours that it was used.

$$1.45 \text{ kilowatts} \cdot 5 \text{ hours} = 7.25 \text{ kilowatt-hours}$$

Shelly's microwave used 7.25 kilowatt-hours last month.

Practice

1. Three people work for a lawn service. It takes them 1.5 hours to service the Campbell's lawn. How many people-hours does it take to service the Campbell's lawn?

   _____ people-hours

2. A car wash has a soap dispenser built into the water line. When the soap cycle is activated, the dispenser releases soap into the water at a rate of 5 L/hr. The dispenser will hold 12.5 L of soap. For how many hours can the soap cycle be activated before the dispenser needs to be refilled?

   _____ hr

3. On a particular day, the exchange rate between U.S. dollars and Italian lira was $1 = 2,125.30 lira. How many U.S. dollars would it take to purchase a shirt that cost 31,879.50 lira?

   $_____

4. Twelve people worked on a project for 8 days. How many people-days were put into the project?

   _____ people-days

5. Kyle is jogging at a rate of 5 mi/hr. How many hours will it take Kyle to jog 1,320 ft?

   _____ hr

   How many minutes will it take Kyle to jog 1,320 ft? _____ min

Scales in Measurement

A **scale** is the ratio of the distance in a model or drawing to the actual distance.

Example

Use the following map. What is the actual distance from Mosquito Flats to Rusty Mountain? (The scale shows that 1 in. = 40 mi.)

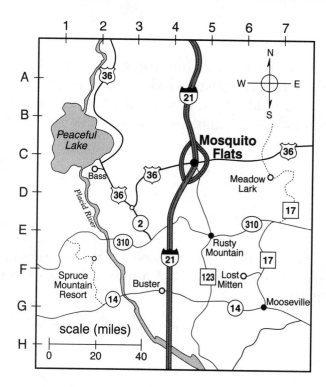

Measure the distance from Mosquito Flats to Rusty Mountain on the map: $\frac{13}{16}$ in. = 0.8125 in.

Multiply by the scale to find the distance. Use dimensional analysis to correctly set up the ratio.

$$0.8125 \text{ in.} \cdot \frac{40 \text{ mi}}{1 \text{ in.}} = 32.5 \text{ mi}$$

The distance from Mosquito Flats to Rusty Mountain is 32.5 miles.

Practice

Directions: Use the map on page 146 to answer Numbers 1 and 2.

1. What is the actual distance from Buster to Mooseville? _____ mi

2. The actual distance from Meadow Lark to Lemon Tree (not included on the map) is 90 miles. How many inches apart would Meadow Lark and Lemon Tree be on the map?

_____ in.

3. The scale of a model race car is 1 in. = 2.25 ft. If the model's length is 8 in., what is the actual length of the race car?

_____ ft

4. In the space provided below, use the scale 1 cm = 3 ft to draw a scale model of a rectangular wall that has a length of 12 ft and a height of 9 ft.

Test Your Skills

1. Jeremy bought 2 liters of juice. About how many **fluid ounces** of juice did Jeremy buy?

   A. 61.48 fl oz
   B. 67.62 fl oz
   C. 73.84 fl oz
   D. 79.06 fl oz

2. Darren has a map with the scale 2 in. = 3 mi. If Darren measures a distance of 4.5 in. on the map, how many miles does that represent?

   A. $1.\overline{3}$ mi
   B. 3.0 mi
   C. 5.25 mi
   D. 6.75 mi

3. California's average July temperature is 75°F. To the nearest degree, what is California's average July temperature in **degrees Celsius**?

   A. 16°C
   B. 20°C
   C. 24°C
   D. 28°C

4. Vic bought 8 gallons of gas. About how many **liters** of gas did Vic buy?

   A. 28.9 L
   B. 30.3 L
   C. 33.8 L
   D. 35.4 L

5. Angie is going to make a huge batch of cookies to take to school. She found a recipe that calls for $4\frac{1}{2}$ cups of milk. How many **pints** of milk does the recipe call for?

   A. $2\frac{1}{4}$ pints

   B. $3\frac{1}{3}$ pints

   C. $4\frac{1}{2}$ pints

   D. 9 pints

6. The density of gold is 19.32 g/cm³. How many grams do you have if you have a 2.5 cm³ chunk of gold?

   A. 36.4 g
   B. 41.7 g
   C. 48.3 g
   D. 50.9 g

7. Julie has a coffeemaker that uses 0.894 kilowatts of energy. She has the timer on the coffeemaker set so that it runs for 2 hours every day. How many kilowatt-hours does the coffeemaker use in a 30-day month?

   A. 86.82 kilowatt-hours
   B. 53.64 kilowatt-hours
   C. 39.48 kilowatt-hours
   D. 26.82 kilowatt-hours

Lesson 10: Geometric Measurement

This lesson reviews the formulas for finding the perimeter and area of two-dimensional figures and the surface area and volume of three-dimensional figures.

Two-Dimensional Figures

Two-dimensional figures can be drawn on a plane. Polygons (such as triangles, quadrilaterals, pentagons, and hexagons) and circles are the most common two-dimensional figures.

Perimeter/circumference

Perimeter (P) is the distance around the outside of a two-dimensional figure. This distance is called the **circumference (C)** when the two-dimensional figure is a circle. The following table shows formulas for finding the perimeter or circumference of some two-dimensional figures.

Figure	Formula	
any polygon ![polygon with sides labeled s_1, s_2, s_3, s_4, s_5]	$P = s_1 + s_2 + s_3 + \ldots + s_n$ (add the lengths of all the sides)	where s_i = length of side i n = number of sides
regular polygon ![hexagon with side labeled l]	$P = l \bullet$ number of sides	where l = length of each side
rectangle ![rectangle with width w and length l]	$P = 2l + 2w$ or $P = 2(l + w)$	where l = length w = width
circle ![circle with radius r and diameter d]	$C = \pi d$ or $C = 2\pi r$	where d = diameter r = radius $\pi \approx 3.14$

 TIP: The numbers lower than the letters are called **subscripts**. They are used to show the different sides of polygons: s_1 means side 1, s_2 means side 2, and so on.

Example

What is the perimeter of the following trapezoid?

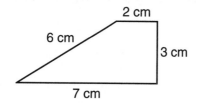

Add the lengths of all the sides.

$P = s_1 + s_2 + s_3 + s_4$

$ = 2 + 3 + 7 + 6$

$ = 18$

The perimeter of the trapezoid is 18 cm.

Example

What is the approximate circumference of the following circle?

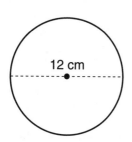

Since the diameter of the circle is given, use $C = \pi d$.

$C = \pi d$

$ \approx 3.14 \bullet 12$

$ \approx 37.68$

The circumference of the circle is approximately 37.68 cm.

Practice

1. What is the perimeter of the following square?

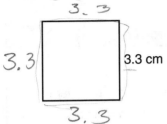

3. 3

3.3

3.3 cm

3. 3

$P =$ _____

2. What is the approximate circumference of the following circle?

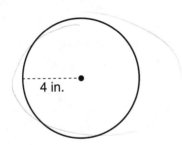

4 in.

$C \approx$ _____

3. What is the perimeter of an equilateral triangle with a side length of 20 cm?

A. 200 cm

B. 100 cm

C. 80 cm

D. 60 cm

4. What is the perimeter of the following parallelogram?

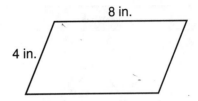

8 in.

4 in.

$P =$ _____

5. What is the perimeter of the following rectangle?

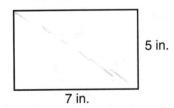

5 in.

7 in.

$P =$ _____

6. What is the perimeter of a stop sign with a side length of 18 in.?

A. 144 in.

B. 128 in.

C. 112 in.

D. 96 in.

Area

Area (**A**) is the measure of the region inside a two-dimensional figure. Area is measured in square units. The following table shows formulas for finding the area of some two-dimensional figures.

Figure	Formula
triangle	$A = \frac{1}{2}bh$ where b = base length h = height
square	$A = s^2$ where s = length of each side
rectangle	$A = lw$ where l = length w = width
parallelogram	$A = bh$ where b = base length h = height
trapezoid	$A = \frac{1}{2}h(b_1 + b_2)$ where b_1 = base 1 length b_2 = base 2 length h = height
circle	$A = \pi r^2$ where r = radius $\pi \approx 3.14$

Example

What is the area of the following trapezoid?

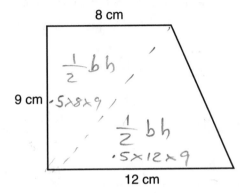

Substitute the values into the formula and solve.

$$A = \frac{1}{2} h(b_1 + b_2)$$

$$= \frac{1}{2} \cdot 9(8 + 12)$$

$$= 90$$

The area of the trapezoid is 90 cm^2.

Example

Johnsville Park is located on a square plot of land with a side length of 1.5 miles. What is the area of Johnsville Park?

Substitute the value into the formula and solve.

$$A = s^2$$

$$= (1.5)^2$$

$$= 2.25$$

The area of Johnsville Park is 2.25 mi^2.

Practice

1. What is the area of a wall with the following dimensions?

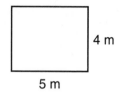

5 m

4 m

$A =$ _____

2. What is the approximate area of a pizza with a radius of 6 in.?

$A \approx$ _____

3. What is the area of a trapezoid with base lengths of 6 cm and 10 cm and a height of 5 cm?

A. 10 cm^2

B. 20 cm^2

C. 40 cm^2

D. 80 cm^2

4. What is the area of the following triangle?

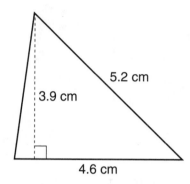

5.2 cm

3.9 cm

4.6 cm

$A =$ _____

5. What is the area of the following parallelogram?

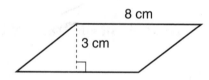

8 cm

3 cm

$A =$ _____

6. If a parallelogram has an area of 90 ft^2 and a height of 6 ft, what is the length of its base?

A. 5 ft

B. 15 ft

C. 24 ft

D. 30 ft

Area of irregular two-dimensional figures

The area of an irregular two-dimensional figure can be found by breaking the figure down into common figures.

Example

What is the approximate area of the following figure?

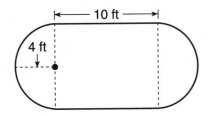

Step 1: **Separate the figure into common figures.**

The figure can be separated into a rectangle and two semicircles. The two semicircles can be put together to form one circle.

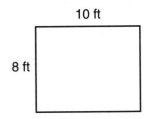   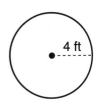

Step 2: **Find the area of each figure.**

Area of rectangle

$A = lw$

$= 8 \cdot 10$

$= 80$

Area of circle

$A = \pi r^2$

$\approx 3.14 \cdot 4^2$

≈ 50.24

Step 3: **Add the areas of each figure.**

$A \approx 80 + 50.24$

≈ 130.24

The area of the figure is approximately 130.24 ft^2.

Practice

Directions: For Numbers 1 through 3, estimate the area, then calculate the actual area.

1.

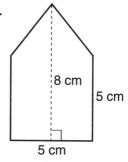

(estimate) $A =$ _____

(actual) $A =$ _____

2.

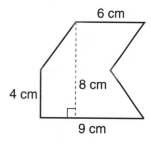

(estimate) $A =$ _____

(actual) $A =$ _____

3.

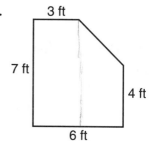

(estimate) $A =$ _____

(actual) $A =$ _____

4. What is the area of the following irregular figure?

6 cm

4 cm   8 cm

9 cm

A. 54 cm^2

B. 60 cm^2

C. 66 cm^2

D. 72 cm^2

5. What is the approximate area of the following irregular figure?

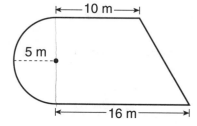

A. 139.25 m^2

B. 169.25 m^2

C. 208.5 m^2

D. 338.5 m^2

Three-Dimensional Figures

Three-dimensional figures are sometimes called space figures. Prisms, cylinders, cones, pyramids, and spheres are the most common three-dimensional figures.

Surface area

Surface area (*S.A.*) is the measure of the outside of a three-dimensional figure. Since it is an area, surface area is measured in squared units. The following table shows formulas for finding the surface area of some three-dimensional figures.

Figure	Formula	
prism	$S.A. = Ph + 2B$	where P = perimeter of the base h = height B = area of the base
cylinder	$S.A. = 2\pi rh + 2\pi r^2$	where r = radius of the base h = height $\pi \approx 3.14$
cone	$S.A. = \pi r \ell + \pi r^2$	where r = radius of the base ℓ = slant height $\pi \approx 3.14$
pyramid	$S.A. = \frac{1}{2} P\ell + B$	where P = perimeter of the base ℓ = slant height B = area of the base
sphere	$S.A. = 4\pi r^2$	where r = radius $\pi \approx 3.14$

 TIP: The bases of a prism or the base of a pyramid can be any polygon.

Example

What is the surface area of the following triangular prism?

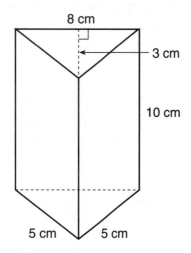

Step 1: **Find the perimeter of one of the bases.**

$$P = 5 + 5 + 8 = 18$$

Step 2: **Find the area of the sides and the area of the bases.**

Area of sides

$$Ph = 18 \cdot 10$$

$$= 180$$

Area of bases

$$2B = 2\left(\frac{1}{2} bh\right)$$

$$= 2\left(\frac{1}{2} \cdot 8 \cdot 3\right)$$

$$= 24$$

Step 3: **Add the area of the sides and the area of the bases.**

$$\textbf{S.A.} = \textbf{Ph + 2B}$$

$$= 180 + 24$$

$$= 204$$

The surface area of the triangular prism is 204 cm^2.

Practice

1. What is the approximate surface area of the following cylinder?

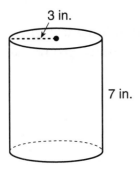

3 in.

7 in.

S.A. ≈ _____

2. What is the surface area of the following rectangular prism?

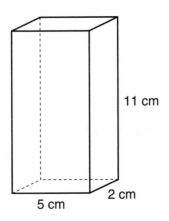

11 cm

2 cm

5 cm

S.A. = _____

3. What is the approximate surface area of an open piece of pipe with a radius of 4 cm and a length of 9 cm?

A. 176.32 cm^2

B. 226.08 cm^2

C. 276.64 cm^2

D. 326.56 cm^2

4. What is the surface area of the following square pyramid?

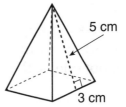

5 cm

3 cm

S.A. = _____

5. What is the approximate surface area of the following cone?

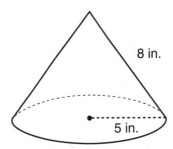

8 in.

5 in.

S.A. ≈ _____

6. What is the approximate surface area of a sphere with a radius of 5 m?

A. 125.6 m^2

B. 188.4 m^2

C. 251.2 m^2

D. 314.0 m^2

Surface area of irregular three-dimensional figures

The surface area of an irregular three-dimensional figure can be found by breaking the figure down into common figures.

Example

What is the approximate surface area of the following figure? Be careful not to include parts of the individual figures that are not on the outside of the original figure.

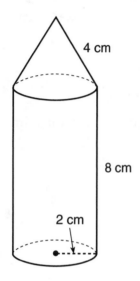

Step 1: **Separate the figure into common figures.**

The figure can be separated into a cone and a cylinder.

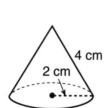
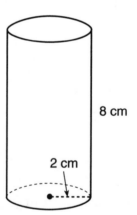

Step 2: **Find the surface area of each figure.** (The base of the cone and one of the bases of the cylinder will not be included.)

Surface Area of cone portion

S.A. = πrℓ

$\approx 3.14 \cdot 2 \cdot 4$

≈ 25.12

Surface Area of cylinder portion

S.A. = 2πrh + πr²

$\approx 2 \cdot 3.14 \cdot 2 \cdot 8 + 3.14 \cdot 2^2$

$\approx 100.48 + 12.56$

≈ 113.04

Step 3: **Add the surface areas of each figure.**

$A \approx 25.12 + 113.04$

≈ 138.16

The surface area of the figure is approximately 138.16 cm².

Practice

Directions: For Numbers 1 and 2, estimate the surface area, then calculate the actual surface area.

1.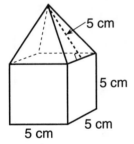

5 cm

5 cm

5 cm

5 cm

2.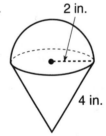

2 in.

4 in.

(estimate) S.A. = _____

(actual) S.A. = _____

(estimate) S.A. = _____

(actual) S.A. ≈ _____

Volume

Volume (V) is the amount of space a three-dimensional figure takes up. It is measured in cubic units. The following table shows formulas for finding the volume of some three-dimensional figures.

Figure	Formula	
prism	$V = Bh$	where B = area of the base h = height
cylinder	$V = \pi r^2 h$	where r = radius of the base h = height $\pi \approx 3.14$
cone	$V = \frac{1}{3}\pi r^2 h$	where r = radius of the base h = height $\pi \approx 3.14$
pyramid	$V = \frac{1}{3}Bh$	where B = area of the base h = height
sphere	$V = \frac{4}{3}\pi r^3$	where r = radius $\pi \approx 3.14$

Example

What is the approximate volume of a ball with a diameter of 9 inches?

Substitute the values into the formula and solve.

$$V = \frac{4}{3}\pi r^3$$

$$\approx \frac{4}{3} \cdot 3.14 \cdot (4.5)^3$$

$$\approx 381.51$$

The volume of a ball with a diameter of 9 inches is approximately 381.51 in.^{3}

Example

What is the approximate volume of the following cone in cm^3? What is the approximate volume of the cone in mm^3? (1 cm^3 = 1,000 mm^3)

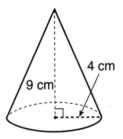

Substitute the values into the formula and solve to find the volume in cm^3.

$$V = \frac{1}{3}\pi r^2 h$$

$$\approx \frac{1}{3} \cdot 3.14 \cdot 4^2 \cdot 9$$

$$\approx 150.72$$

The volume of the cone is approximately 150.72 cm^3.

Use the conversion ratio $\left(\dfrac{1{,}000 \text{ mm}^3}{1 \text{ cm}^3}\right)$ to convert to mm^3.

$$150.72 \text{ cm}^3 \cdot \frac{1{,}000 \text{ mm}^3}{1 \text{ cm}^3} = 150{,}720 \text{ mm}^3.$$

The volume of the cone is approximately 150,720 mm^3.

Practice

1. What is the approximate volume of the following sphere?

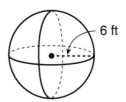

$V \approx$ _____

2. What is the approximate volume of the following cylinder?

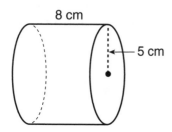

$V \approx$ _____

3. What is the approximate volume of a cone with a radius of 4 in. and a height of 15 in.?

A. 125.6 in.^{3}
B. 188.4 in.^{3}
C. 251.2 in.^{3}
D. 314.0 in.^{3}

4. What is the volume of the following triangular prism?

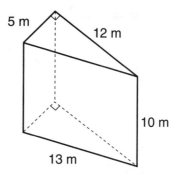

$V =$ _____

5. What is the volume of the following square pyramid?

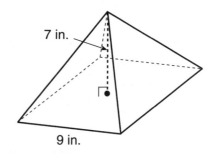

$V =$ _____

6. What is the volume of a rectangular prism in **ft^3**, with a length of 5 yd, a width of 16 yd, and a height of 10 yd? ($1 \text{ yd}^3 = 27 \text{ ft}^3$)

A.   800 ft^3
B.   2,400 ft^3
C.   7,200 ft^3
D. 21,600 ft^3

Building three-dimensional figures from cubes

You can form irregular three-dimensional figures by putting together any number of same-sized cubes. The surface area of such a figure is found by multiplying the number of squares that make up the surface of the figure by the area of each square. The volume is found by multiplying the number of cubes that make up the figure by the volume of each cube.

Example

What is the surface area and volume of the following figure?

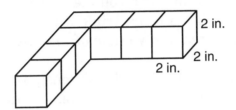

There are 30 squares that make up the surface of the figure. The area of each square is 2^2 or 4 in.^{2}

$S.A. = 30 \cdot 4 = 120$

The surface area of the figure is 120 in.^{2}

There are 7 cubes that make up the figure. The volume of each cube is 2^3 or 8 in.^{3}

$V = 7 \cdot 8 = 56$

The volume of the figure is 56 in.^{3}

Practice

Directions: For Numbers 1 and 2, find the surface area and volume of each figure.

1.

2.

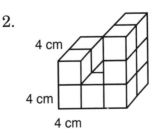

S.A. = _____ V = _____   S.A. = _____ V = _____

Changes in dimensions

When all the dimensions of a three-dimensional figure increase or decrease by the same scale factor (all the dimensions are multiplied by the same number), the new surface area and volume can be determined using the scale factor. The surface area of the new figure is the square of the scale factor times the surface area of the original figure. The volume of the new figure is the cube of the scale factor times the volume of the original figure.

 Example

The surface area of Prism I is 236 m². The volume of Prism I is 240 m². If the dimensions of Prism II are triple the dimensions of Prism I, what is the surface area and volume of Prism II?

Since the dimensions of Prism II are triple the dimensions of Prism I, the scale factor is 3. To find the surface area of Prism II, multiply the surface area of Prism I by the **square** of the scale factor.

$$S.A. = 236 \bullet 3^2$$
$$= 236 \bullet 9$$
$$= 2{,}124$$

The surface area of Prism II is 2,124 m².

To find the volume of Prism II, multiply the volume of Prism I by the **cube** of the scale factor.

$$S.A. = 240 \bullet 3^3$$
$$= 240 \bullet 27$$
$$= 6{,}480$$

The surface area of Prism II is 6,480 m³.

Practice

1. What is the approximate surface area and volume of a cylinder with a radius of 2 cm and a height of 5 cm?

   $S.A. \approx$ _____

   $V \approx$ _____

2. What is the approximate surface area and volume of a cylinder with dimensions that are twice those of the cylinder in Number 1?

   $S.A. \approx$ _____

   $V \approx$ _____

3. The surface area of Pyramid I is 96 cm^2. The volume of Pyramid I is 48 cm^3. If the dimensions of Pyramid II are half the dimensions of Pyramid I, what is the surface area and volume of Pyramid II?

   $S.A. \approx$ _____

   $V \approx$ _____

4. The approximate volume of Sphere 1 is 904.32 cm^3. The radius of Sphere 2 is triple the radius of Sphere 1. What is the approximate volume of Sphere 2?

   A. 2,712.96 cm^3
   B. 8,138.88 cm^3
   C. 16,277.76 cm^3
   D. 24,416.64 cm^3

5. The approximate surface area of Cone 1 is 351.68 in.^{2} The approximate surface area of Cone 2 is 5,626.88 in.^{2} By what scale factor have the dimensions of Cone 1 been multiplied to produce Cone 2?

   A. 2
   B. 3
   C. 4
   D. 5

Test Your Skills

1. What is the approximate surface area of a cone with a radius of 5 in. and a slant height of 7 in.?

    A. 109.9 in.^{2}

    B. 125.6 in.^{2}

    C. 141.3 in.^{2}

    D. 188.4 in.^{2}

2. Randy wants to find the circumference of one of his bicycle tires. The diameter of the tire is 60 cm. What is the approximate circumference of the tire?

    A. 188.4 cm

    B. 376.8 cm

    C. 753.6 cm

    D. 2,826.1 cm

3. What is the approximate area of the following figure?

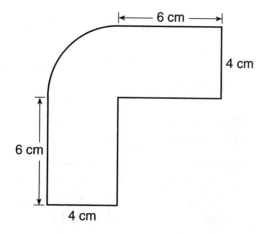

    A. 54.28 cm^2

    B. 60.56 cm^2

    C. 66.84 cm^2

    D. 73.12 cm^2

4. Approximately how much water would it take to completely fill a circular wading pool with a radius of 3 ft and a height of 1.5 ft?

    A. 14.13 ft^3

    B. 21.195 ft^3

    C. 42.39 ft^3

    D. 63.585 ft^3

5. Which figure has the same area as a trapezoid with base lengths of 6 m and 10 m and a height of 5 m?

    A. a circle with a radius of 4 m

    B. a rectangle with a length of 2 m and a width of 10 m

    C. a triangle with a base length of 16 m and a height of 5 m

    D. a parallelogram with a base length of 10 m and a height of 8 m

6. A shipping company has 2 sizes of boxes. The dimensions of the larger box are twice the dimensions of the smaller box. The volume of the larger box is 96 ft^3. What is the volume of the smaller box?

    A. 12 ft^3

    B. 24 ft^3

    C. 36 ft^3

    D. 48 ft^3

7. The following triangle has an area of 280 mm².

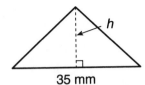

35 mm

What is the height of the triangle?

A. 2 mm
B. 8 mm
C. 12 mm
D. 16 mm

8. What is the volume of the following figure?

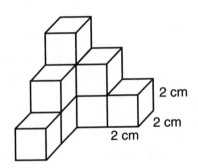

2 cm

2 cm

2 cm

A.   56 cm³
B.   72 cm³
C.   88 cm³
D. 104 cm³

9. What is the perimeter of the following trapezoid?

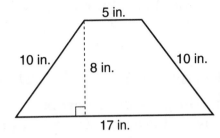

5 in.

10 in.   8 in.   10 in.

17 in.

A. 42 in.
B. 50 in.
C. 80 in.
D. 88 in.

10. What is the approximate surface area of a cylindrical drinking glass with a diameter of 9 cm and a height of 12 cm?

A. 402.705 cm²
B. 579.33 cm²
C. 755.955 cm²
D. 932.58 cm²

11. A football field (including the end zones) is 360 feet long and 160 feet wide. What is the area of the football field?

A.   1,040 ft²
B.   6,400 ft²
C. 52,120 ft²
D. 57,600 ft²

Lesson 11: Geometric Concepts

This lesson reviews the Pythagorean Theorem, congruency, transformations, and the coordinate plane.

Pythagorean Theorem

The **Pythagorean Theorem** states that for any right triangle, the square of the length of the hypotenuse is equal to the sum of the squares of the lengths of the legs.

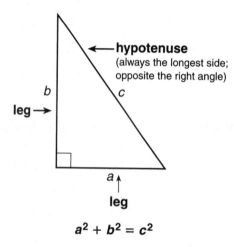

$$a^2 + b^2 = c^2$$

Example

What is the value of b in the following right triangle?

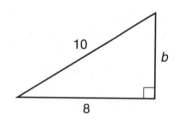

$$a^2 + b^2 = c^2$$
$$8^2 + b^2 = 10^2$$
$$64 + b^2 = 100$$
$$b^2 = 36$$
$$b = 6 \qquad \text{(Find the square root of both sides.)}$$

The value of b is 6 units.

Converse of the Pythagorean Theorem

The **converse of the Pythagorean Theorem** allows you to use the side lengths of a triangle to determine whether a triangle is a right triangle. Substitute the values into the Pythagorean Theorem, then simplify. If the equation is true, the triangle is a right triangle. Remember to substitute the longest given side for c.

Example

Is a triangle with side lengths 5 in., 10 in., and 13 in. a right triangle?

Substitute 5 and 10 for a or b and 13 for c, then simplify.

$$a^2 + b^2 = c^2$$
$$5^2 + 10^2 = 13^2$$
$$25 + 100 = 169$$
$$125 \neq 169$$

The triangle **is not** a right triangle.

Example

Is a triangle with side lengths 7 cm, 24 cm, and 25 cm a right triangle?

Substitute 7 and 24 for a or b and 25 for c, then simplify.

$$a^2 + b^2 = c^2$$
$$7^2 + 24^2 = 25^2$$
$$49 + 576 = 625$$
$$625 = 625 \quad \textbf{true}$$

The triangle **is** a right triangle.

Practice

Directions: For Numbers 1 and 2, find the length of the third side for each triangle.

1.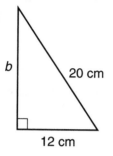

$b =$ _____

2.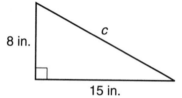

$c =$ _____

Directions: For Numbers 3 through 6, determine if the triangle with the given side lengths is a right triangle.

3. 3 in., 4 in., and 5 in.

4. 10 mm, 10 mm, and 12 mm

5. 5 cm, 6 cm, and 7 cm

6. 20 ft, 21 ft, and 29 ft

Congruent Figures

Congruent figures have the **same shape and the same size**. All corresponding segments and angles are congruent.

Given: $\triangle ABC \cong \triangle DFE$

$\overline{AB} \cong \overline{DF}$

$\overline{AC} \cong \overline{DE}$

$\overline{BC} \cong \overline{FE}$

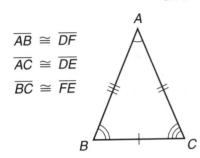

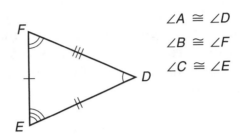

$\angle A \cong \angle D$

$\angle B \cong \angle F$

$\angle C \cong \angle E$

 **Practice**

Directions: Use the following information to answer Numbers 1 through 5.

Given: $ABCDEF \cong JKLMNO$

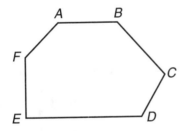

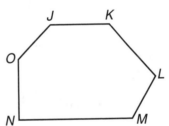

1. Which angle in *ABCDEF* is congruent to $\angle M$?_____

2. $\overline{BC} \cong$ _____

3. $\overline{EF} \cong$ _____

4. Which pair of sides are congruent?

    A. $\overline{AB}$ and $\overline{NO}$

    B. $\overline{CD}$ and $\overline{LM}$

    C. $\overline{FA}$ and $\overline{AB}$

    D. $\overline{OJ}$ and $\overline{CD}$

5. Which pair of angles are congruent?

    A. $\angle A$ and $\angle J$

    B. $\angle B$ and $\angle D$

    C. $\angle C$ and $\angle O$

    D. $\angle F$ and $\angle L$

Transformations

Translations, rotations, and reflections are transformations that are performed on geometric figures.

Translation

When you slide a figure without changing anything other than its position, you perform a **translation**. Figures with **translational symmetry** can be translated in a specified direction so that one figure lands on top of an identical figure.

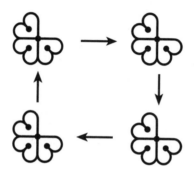

Rotation

When you turn a figure either clockwise or counterclockwise about a certain point, you perform a **rotation**. $\frac{1}{4}$ turn = 90°, $\frac{1}{2}$ turn = 180°, and $\frac{3}{4}$ turn = 270°. A full turn is equal to 360°. A figure has **rotational symmetry** if it can be rotated so that its rotated image coincides with the original figure after turning less than 360°. The following are clockwise rotations.

original
position

90° rotation
($\frac{1}{4}$ turn)

180° rotation
($\frac{1}{2}$ turn)

270° rotation
($\frac{3}{4}$ turn)

360° rotation
(full turn)

Reflection

When you flip a figure and create its mirror image, you perform a **reflection**. When a figure is reflected, there must be a **line of reflection**, or a **line of symmetry**. A figure has **reflectional symmetry** if it falls back onto itself after a reflection has been performed.

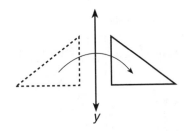

Some figures have no type of symmetry. These figures are called **asymmetric**.

 Practice

Directions: Write which type of symmetry or symmetries is shown for each figure in Numbers 1 through 3. If the figure has no symmetry, write "asymmetric" on the line.

1.

_____

2.

_____

3.

_____

4. Write the degree of clockwise or counterclockwise rotation from Figure 1 to Figure 2.

Figure 1   Figure 2

_____

5. Which figure is asymmetric?

A.

B.

C.

D.

Coordinate Plane

The coordinate plane has a horizontal axis (called the *x*-axis) and a vertical axis (called the *y*-axis). The point where the two axes intersect is called the **origin**. The coordinate plane is divided into four **quadrants**.

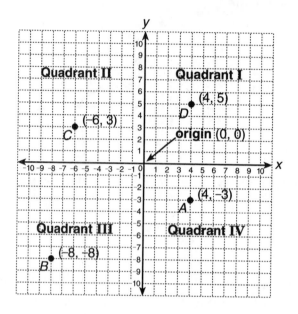

Points on the coordinate plane are described by ordered pairs (also known as coordinates). The first number describes a point's location on the *x*-axis. The second number describes its location on the *y*-axis.

 Example

(4, 5) is located in Quadrant I. All points in Quadrant I are (+, +).

Points in Quadrants II, III, and IV are as follows:

Quadrant II: (−, +)   Point *C*: (−6, 3)

Quadrant III: (−, −)   Point *B*: (−8, −8)

Quadrant IV: (+, −)   Point *A*: (4, −3)

Practice

Directions: Use the following coordinate plane to answer Numbers 1 through 7.

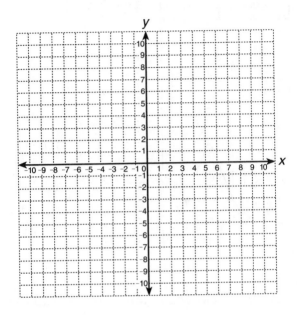

1. Plot the following points: A: $(-9, 8)$, B: $(-5, 8)$, C: $(-5, 4)$, D: $(-9, 4)$.

2. Connect the points and describe the figure. _____

3. What is the perimeter of the figure? _____

4. What is the area of the figure? _____

5. On the coordinate plane, translate the figure 11 units to the right and 3 units down. Label the new points as A' (read "A prime"), B', C', and D'.

6. What are the coordinates of A' and B'?

   A. $(-6, -3)$, $(-2, -3)$
   B. $(2, -3)$, $(6, -3)$
   C. $(1, 4)$, $(5, 4)$
   D. $(2, 5)$, $(6, 5)$

7. What are the coordinates of C' and D'?

   A. $(8, 3)$, $(4, 3)$
   B. $(6, 1)$, $(2, 1)$
   C. $(6, -7)$, $(2, -7)$
   D. $(-2, -7)$, $(-6, -7)$

Directions: Use the following coordinate plane to answer Numbers 8 and 9.

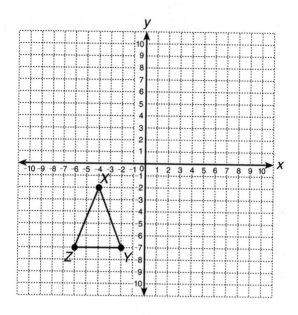

8. Rotate triangle *XYZ* 90° clockwise about point *X*. Label the new points *Y′* and *Z′*.

9. What are the new coordinates? *Y′* _____ *Z′* _____

10. On the following coordinate plane, reflect the figure about the *y*-axis. Label the new points as *H′*, *I′*, *J′*, *K′*, and *L′*.

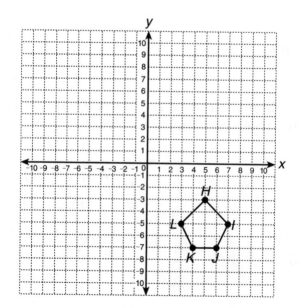

Test Your Skills

Directions: Use the following coordinate plane to answer Numbers 1 and 2.

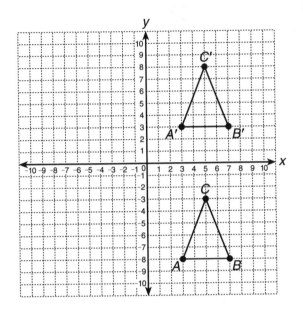

Directions: Use the following figures to answer Numbers 3 and 4.

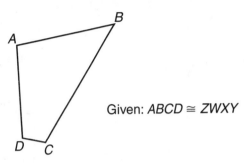

Given: $ABCD \cong ZWXY$

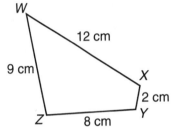

1. What kind of transformation was performed on triangle ABC to form triangle $A'B'C'$?

   A. asymmetric
   B. translation
   C. reflection
   D. rotation

2. Which of the following describes the movement of triangle ABC?

   A. left 0, up 10
   B. left 1, up 11
   C. right 1, up 10
   D. right 0, up 11

3. Which angle in $WXYZ$ is congruent to $\angle C$?

   A. $\angle W$
   B. $\angle X$
   C. $\angle Y$
   D. $\angle Z$

4. What is the length of $\overline{AB}$?

   A. 2 cm
   B. 8 cm
   C. 9 cm
   D. 12 cm

5. What is the area of △WXY on the following coordinate plane?

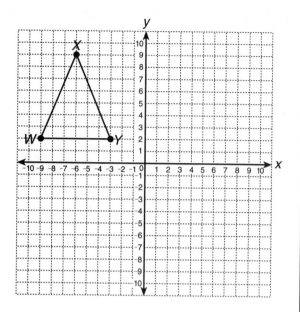

A. 21 units^2
B. 42 units^2
C. 21 units^3
D. 42 units^3

6. What is the value of a in the following right triangle?

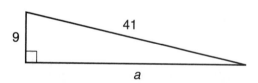

A. 32
B. 35
C. 38
D. 40

7. When the following figure is rotated $\frac{3}{4}$ turn clockwise, what does it look like?

A.

B.

C.

D.

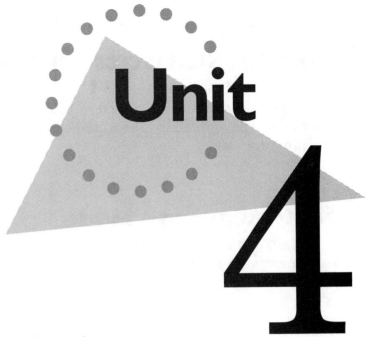

Unit 4

Statistics, Data Analysis, and Probability

Many business decisions are based on data analysis. Business reports often display data in tables, charts, graphs, or some kind of plot. A presentation about the data is given to help explain the report. Businesspeople can then analyze the data and make a decision.

In this unit, you will display data that have one or more variables in a variety of ways, including frequency tables, bar graphs, histograms, line graphs, circle graphs, and scatterplots. You will analyze the data to determine relationships between the variables. You will also determine probabilities to make predictions about events.

In This Unit

Statistics and Data Analysis

Probability

Lesson 12: Statistics and Data Analysis

Statistics is a set of methods used to collect, organize, describe, and analyze numerical data. Data can be displayed in tables, graphs, and plots. After deciding which type of display to use, you can analyze a single data set or compare two data sets.

Mean, Median, and Mode

Mean, median, and mode are **measures of central tendency** that use one number to represent all the numbers in a data set.

Mean

The **mean** (average) is the sum of the numbers in a group divided by how many numbers are in that group. It is affected by all the numbers in the set.

Median

The **median** is the middle number in a group of numbers arranged in order of value. If the number of data values is odd, the median is simply the middle value. If the number of data values is even, the median is the average of the two middle values.

Mode

The **mode** is the number that appears most often in a data set. There may be one mode, more than one mode (if two or more values appear most often), or no mode at all (if no value appears more than once in the set).

Example

Find the mean, median, and mode of the following data set.

72, 73, 73, 73, 77, 79, 84, 85, 85, 89

$$\text{mean} = \frac{72 + 73 + 73 + 73 + 77 + 79 + 84 + 85 + 85 + 89}{10} = \frac{790}{10} = \textbf{79}$$

$$\text{median} = \frac{77 + 79}{2} = \textbf{78}$$

$$\text{mode} = \textbf{73}$$

Practice

Directions: For Numbers 1 through 3, find the mean, median, and mode(s) of each data set.

1. 25, 94, 47, 82, 19, 36, 47

   mean: _____ median: _____ mode(s): _____

2. 52, 125, 176, 36, 95, 22, 202, 100

   mean: _____ median: _____ mode(s): _____

3. 246, 172, 216, 187, 246, 984, 301, 216

   mean: _____ median: _____ mode(s): _____

4. The following table shows the scores that Tianna received on seven English tests.

English Test Scores

Test	1	2	3	4	5	6	7
Score	71	82	79	85	70	70	82

Find the mean, median, and mode(s) of Tianna's test scores.

mean: _____ median: _____ mode(s): _____

Frequency Tables

A **frequency table** is a list of items that shows the number of times, or frequency, each item occurs. Results from a survey can easily be recorded in a frequency table.

Example

The following list shows the number of wins the Raiders had each football season from 1960 through 2000.

6, 2, 1, 10, 5, 8, 8, 13, 12, 12, 8, 8, 10, 9, 12, 11, 13, 11, 9, 9, 11, 7, 8, 12, 11, 12, 8, 5, 7, 8, 12, 9, 7, 10, 9, 8, 7, 4, 8, 8, 12

The following frequency table organizes the data from the list. The numbers of tallies, called the frequencies, are listed in the third column.

Raiders' Wins

Number of Wins	Tally	Frequency
1	I	1
2	I	1
3		0
4	I	1
5	II	2
6	I	1
7	IIII	4
8	IIII IIII	10
9	IIII	5
10	III	3
11	IIII	4
12	IIII II	7
13	II	2

The numbers of wins are listed in numerical order in the first column. Even though there was not a season when the Raiders won exactly three games, it is still represented in the table with a frequency of zero.

185

Practice

1. Organize the data from the following list of student test scores in the frequency table.

    89, 74, 96, 85, 79, 56, 97, 91, 90, 86, 93, 84, 82, 85, 77, 76, 80, 68, 87, 65, 99, 95, 88, 82, 85, 94, 73, 78, 79, 58, 67, 84, 90, 90, 88, 79, 82, 91

Test Scores

Score	Tally	Frequency
90–100		
80–89		
70–79		
60–69		
50–59		

Directions: Use the the frequency table you created in Number 1 to answer Numbers 2 through 7.

2. How many students are represented in the frequency table? _____

3. If each student needed a score of 60 or higher to pass the test, how many students passed the test?

    _____

4. How many students received a score of at least 70? _____

5. In which score interval did the least number of students score?

    _____

6. In which score interval did the greatest number of students score?

    A. 60–69
    B. 70–79
    C. 80–89
    D. 90–100

7. How many students received a score lower than 80?

    A. 8
    B. 13
    C. 14
    D. 25

Bar Graphs

A **bar graph** is used to compare amounts. A bar graph uses vertical or horizontal bars to show data.

Example

For extra credit, Katie found out on what day of the week each student in her school was born. She organized her results in the following frequency table.

Students' Birthdays

Day	Frequency
Sunday	39
Monday	18
Tuesday	86
Wednesday	49
Thursday	54
Friday	73
Saturday	72

The following bar graph displays the data from the frequency table. The heights of the bars represent the frequencies.

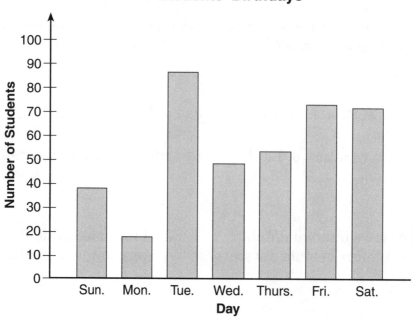

The bar graph makes it easy to compare the data values.

Practice

1. Mr. Smith asked his tenth-grade students which color of a rainbow they liked the best. Here are their responses.

    blue, green, red, green, blue, yellow, violet, red, red, violet, blue, red, blue, red, violet, indigo, green, blue, red, yellow, red, green, violet, orange, yellow, blue, violet, red, green, red, blue, orange

Organize the data in the following frequency table.

Favorite Rainbow Colors

Color	Tally	Frequency
Red		
Orange		
Yellow		
Green		
Blue		
Indigo		
Violet		

Display the data from the frequency table in a bar graph.

Favorite Rainbow Colors

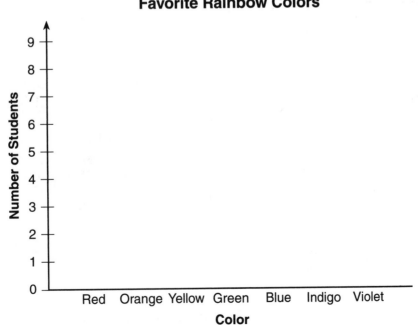

Directions: Use the frequency table and bar graph you created in Number 1 to answer Numbers 2 through 9.

2. How many students are in Mr. Smith's tenth-grade class? _____

3. What color did the greatest number of students like the best? _____

   How many students liked that color the best? _____

4. What color did the least number of students like the best? _____

   How many students liked that color the best? _____

5. What two colors did the same number of students like the best?

   _____

6. How many more students liked red rather than indigo the best?

   _____

7. What is your favorite color of the rainbow? _____

   How many students in Mr. Smith's class have the same favorite color of the rainbow as you?

   _____

8. What color did exactly two students like the best?

   A. blue
   B. indigo
   C. yellow
   D. orange

9. What two colors combined did half of the class like the best?

   A. red and blue
   B. indigo and red
   C. yellow and blue
   D. indigo and violet

Histograms

A **histogram** is a type of bar graph that is used to show continuous data. The bars of a histogram are always vertical and always touching. The heights of the bars represent the frequencies.

Example

The following frequency table shows the number of states that entered the Union in twenty-year intervals.

States' Entries into Union

Year	Frequency
1780–1799	16
1800–1819	6
1820–1839	4
1840–1859	7
1860–1879	5
1880–1899	7
1900–1919	3
1920–1939	0
1940–1959	2

The following histogram displays the data from the frequency table.

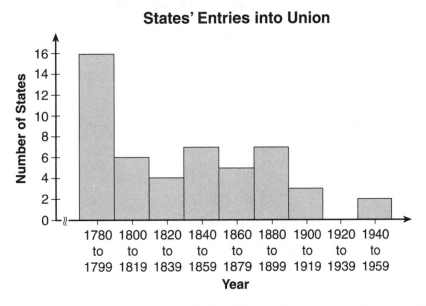

Notice that no states entered the Union between 1920 and 1939. That information is represented by a zero in the frequency table, and there is no bar drawn in the histogram. (If you find yourself trying to remember where California fits in, it became a state in 1850.)

Practice

1. The students in Miss Wagner's gym class ran the one-mile run for the fitness test. They recorded the following times (in minutes and seconds).

   6:44, 8:21, 7:30, 7:05, 6:52, 7:18, 6:39, 8:48, 7:25, 7:35, 6:12, 8:02, 7:01, 6:59, 6:01, 7:46, 7:10, 6:40, 7:34, 8:07, 9:21, 7:16, 7:25, 6:23

Organize the data in the following frequency table.

One-Mile Run

Time (min:sec)	Tally	Frequency
6:00–6:29		
6:30–6:59		
7:00–7:29		
7:30–7:59		
8:00–8:29		
8:30–8:59		
9:00–9:29		

Display the data from the frequency table in a histogram.

One-Mile Run

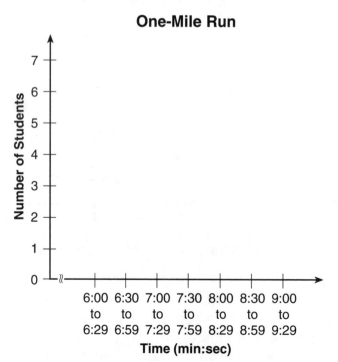

Directions: Use the frequency table and histogram you created in Number 1 to answer Numbers 2 through 7.

2. How many students ran the one-mile run? _____

3. How many students ran faster than: 6 minutes? _____

7 minutes? _____

8 minutes? _____

9 minutes? _____

10 minutes? _____

4. In which time interval did the greatest number of students run?

_____

5. If you wanted to know what each student's time was, would you be able to tell by looking at the histogram only? Explain.

_____

_____

_____

6. How many students ran the mile in 8 minutes or longer?

A. 1
B. 3
C. 5
D. 19

7. In which time interval did exactly one-sixth of the students run?

A. 6:00–6:29
B. 6:30–6:59
C. 7:30–7:59
D. 8:30–8:59

Line Graphs

A **line graph** is a graph that shows changes over time. Sometimes line graphs show a **trend** that describes what the data might look like as time goes on.

Example

The following table shows the prices of a general admission ticket at a movie theater for ten years.

Ticket Prices

Year	Price
1993	$7.25
1994	$7.50
1995	$7.75
1996	$7.75
1997	$8.00
1998	$8.00
1999	$8.25
2000	$8.50
2001	$8.50
2002	$8.75

The following line graph displays the data from the table.

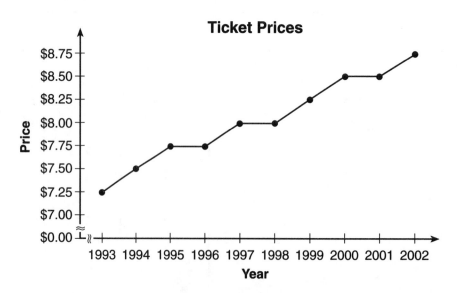

The graph shows a trend of increasing prices for movie tickets. A good prediction that can be made from the graph is that the price of a movie ticket will continue to increase each year.

Practice

1. Carla is reading a 250-page book. The following table shows the page number at which she stopped reading at the end of each day.

Book Log

Day	Page Number
1	20
2	45
3	55
4	85
5	85
6	120
7	160
8	180
9	190
10	240

Display the data from the table in a line graph.

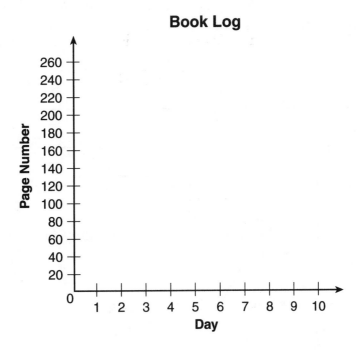

Directions: Use the table and line graph you created in Number 1 to answer Numbers 2 through 9.

2. On what day did Carla read the greatest number of pages? _____

   How many pages did Carla read that day? _____

3. On what day did Carla read the least number of pages? _____

   How many pages did Carla read that day? _____

4. On what day did Carla pass the halfway point of the book? _____

5. By the end of the 10th day, how many more pages does Carla have to read to finish the book?

   _____

6. On what day will Carla most likely finish reading the book? _____

7. If Carla decides to read a 320-page book next, how many days do you think it will take her to finish reading it? Explain.

   _____

   _____

   _____

   _____

8. On what two days did Carla read exactly 10 pages of her book?

   A. Day 2 and Day 8
   B. Day 3 and Day 9
   C. Day 5 and Day 8
   D. Day 8 and Day 9

9. How many pages did Carla read on Day 2?

   A. 25
   B. 30
   C. 45
   D. 55

Circle Graphs

A **circle graph** is a graph that represents parts of a whole. The sum of all the parts of the graph must equal 100%, or 1.

Example

While Tyler sat on the front porch for an hour one day, he kept track of all the different types of vehicles that drove by his house. He put his information in the following table.

Vehicle Distribution

Vehicle Type	Number	Percent
Car	45	39.8%
S.U.V.	38	33.6%
Truck	20	17.7%
Van	8	7.1%
Other	2	1.8%

The following circle graph displays the data from the table.

Vehicle Distribution

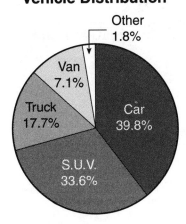

Notice that the sum of all the percentages is equal to 100%.

Practice

1. Of the 200 boxes of fruit that the students in Miss Violetta's class sold, 27% were apples, 8% were grapefruit, 3% were pears, 40% were oranges, and 22% were a combination of the four fruits. Display the data in a circle graph.

Fruit Boxes Sold

Directions: Use the circle graph you created in Number 1 to answer Numbers 2 through 6.

2. Of what kind of fruit did the students sell the greatest number of boxes?

_____

3. How many boxes of apples did the students sell? _____

4. What percentage of the boxes did not have any oranges in them?

_____

5. How many more boxes of grapefruit were sold than pears?

   A. 5
   B. 8
   C. 10
   D. 11

6. What two kinds of fruit combined for 35% of the boxes sold?

   A. apples and pears
   B. pears and oranges
   C. apples and grapefruit
   D. grapefruit and oranges

Scatterplots

A **scatterplot** is a graph that shows the correlation (relationship) between two data sets. The data are plotted on a graph as ordered pairs.

The closer the points on the scatterplot come to forming a straight line, the stronger they are correlated. If the scatterplot shows a straight line with a slope of 1 or −1, the scatterplot shows **perfect correlation**. If both data sets are increasing, the scatterplot shows **positive correlation**. If one data set is increasing while the other is decreasing, the scatterplot shows **negative correlation**. If the data sets show no relationship, the scatterplot shows **no correlation**. The points will be randomly scattered.

When data sets have a positive or negative correlation, a **trend line** can be drawn to approximate the data. The trend line is drawn in such a way that there is about the same number of points above the line as below the line.

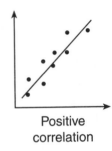

Positive correlation

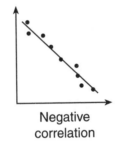

Negative correlation

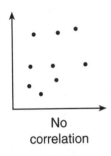

No correlation

Example

The following table shows the number of hours a student studied for each of seven biology tests and the score received on each test. The following scatterplot shows the data from the table.

Study Time (in hours)	Score
1.5	80
3.0	90
1.0	70
2.5	88
1.5	85
3.5	96
4.0	100

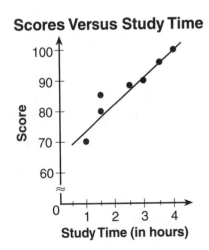

Most of the points lie very close to the trend line, which indicates that the two variables, study time and test score, are strongly correlated. The slope of the trend line is positive, which means the variables have a positive correlation. The greater the number of hours the student studied, the higher the test score he or she received.

Practice

Directions: Use the following table to answer Numbers 1 through 3.

Math Score Versus Hours of Sleep

Hours of Sleep	9	4	7	6	6	8	9	8	5	7	8	7
Math Test Score	93	71	84	77	82	93	91	100	70	83	90	90

1. Display the data in a scatterplot. Then draw a trend line.

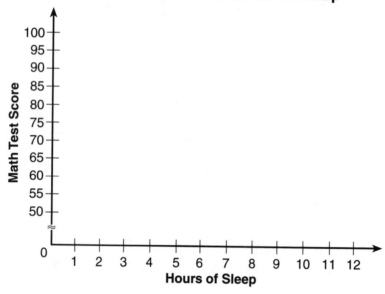

2. In what ways are the variables correlated?

   A. weakly and negatively

   B. weakly and positively

   C. strongly and negatively

   D. strongly and positively

3. What test score do you predict a student who slept for 4.5 hours would most likely receive?

   A. 50

   B. 60

   C. 70

   D. 80

Claims from Data

Once data has been collected and displayed, it is time to make some **claims** about the data. A claim is a statement about the data that may or may not be true. A person can claim that he or she is the oldest person in the world, even though it may be proven that someone else is older. A claim that is **true** is called **valid**. A claim that is **not true** is called **invalid**.

Example

Jeff did a survey to find out which season of the year tenth-graders of Anytown, California, like the best. He asked all 350 tenth-graders of Anytown what season of the year they like best. Here are the results:

Spring–70

Summer–180

Fall–80

Winter–20

Jeff claims that more than twice as many tenth-graders in Anytown, California, like summer better than fall. Is his claim valid or invalid?

Take the number of people who like fall (80) and multiply it by 2.

$80 \times 2 = 160$

Compare the number of students who like summer (180) with 160. Is 180 > 160? Yes, it is. Therefore, Jeff's claim is valid.

Example

A survey showed that, when asked which day of the week is their favorite, 42% of the people said Saturday. Robert claims that 42% of the people surveyed work on weekdays. Is his claim valid or invalid?

It is invalid. The survey did not mention anything about working or not working. Just because people like Saturday, we can't assume that they like it because they don't have to work.

This example shows that you need to read the claim carefully and check that the data supports what is being said.

Practice

Directions: For Numbers 1 through 5, decide if the claim is valid or invalid based on the given information. Circle the correct answer.

1. Four out of five dentists recommend Gerry's Sticky Icky Gum to prevent cavities.

   Claim: Four out of five dentists chew gum.

   valid   invalid

2. Fifty percent of all Spanish speakers in the United States come from Spanish-speaking countries.

   Claim: One-half of all Spanish speakers in the United States come from Spanish-speaking countries.

   valid   invalid

3. Three percent of all new cars have defective parts.

   Claim: If you buy a new car, it most likely does not have any defective parts.

   valid   invalid

4. The following percentages show the results of the election for mayor.

   Joan Peterson–51%

   Ralph MacDonald–32%

   Stephan Bure–17%

   Claim: More women than men voted in the election.

   valid   invalid

5. In a national taste test, 63% of the people surveyed chose the taste of diet soda over the taste of regular soda.

   Claim: Diet soda is better for you than regular soda.

   valid   invalid

Test Your Skills

1. In what way are the variables represented by the following scatterplot correlated?

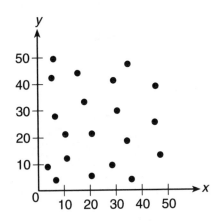

   A. The two variables are not correlated.
   B. The two variables are perfectly correlated.
   C. The two variables are positively correlated.
   D. The two variables are negatively correlated.

2. Of 100 people surveyed, 37 said they read at least two books a month. Which claim is valid?

   A. 63 of the people surveyed read three or more books a month.
   B. 63 of the people surveyed go to the library at least two times a month.
   C. 63 of the people surveyed read no books or one book a month.
   D. 63 of the people surveyed cannot read.

Directions: Use the following information to answer Numbers 3 and 4.

The following circle graph shows the percent of sales at a school store.

School Store Sales

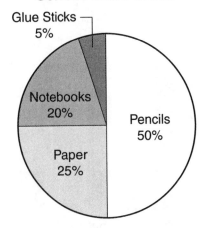

3. Which three items combine to account for 50% of the store's sales?

   A. pencils, paper, and notebooks
   B. glue sticks, pencils, and paper
   C. paper, notebooks, and glue sticks
   D. notebooks, glue sticks, and pencils

4. If the sales totaled $250, how much did the sales of notebooks total?

   A. $40
   B. $50
   C. $60
   D. $70

Directions: Use the following information to answer Numbers 5 and 6.

The following double bar graph shows the results of the last mayor election by the number of votes cast by males and females.

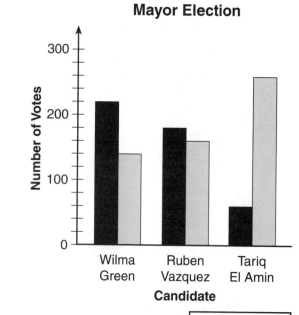

Mayor Election

KEY
■ = Male
▨ = Female

5. How many more females than males voted in the election?

   A. 40
   B. 60
   C. 80
   D. 100

6. Who received the most votes, and how many more votes did he or she receive than the person with the next highest number of votes?

   A. Wilma Green, 20 votes
   B. Tariq El Amin, 10 votes
   C. Tariq El Amin, 30 votes
   D. Ruben Vazquez, 20 votes

Directions: Use the following information to answer Numbers 7 and 8.

The following histogram shows the number of wins for each major league baseball team in the same season.

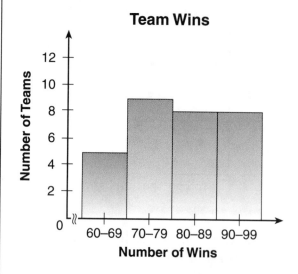

7. How many teams won at least 80 games?

   A. 8
   B. 11
   C. 14
   D. 16

8. Which statement is **not** true?

   A. There are 30 teams represented by the histogram.
   B. The least number of teams won less than 70 games.
   C. There were twice as many teams that won 70–79 games as there were teams that won 60–69 games.
   D. The number of teams that won 80–89 games was the same as the number of teams that won 90–99 games.

Directions: Use the following information to answer Numbers 9 and 10.

The following line graph shows school enrollment for a six-year time period.

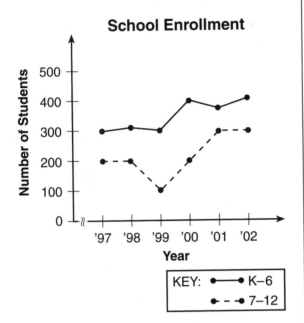

School Enrollment

KEY: ●——● K–6
●– –● 7–12

9. About how many more students were enrolled in K–6 than 7–12 in 2000?

A. 100
B. 150
C. 200
D. 250

10. In what year was the difference between students enrolled in K–6 and 7–12 the least?

A. 2001
B. 2000
C. 1998
D. 1997

Directions: Use the following table to answer Numbers 11 through 13.

Day	High Temperature
Sunday	89°F
Monday	85°F
Tuesday	87°F
Wednesday	80°F
Thursday	81°F
Friday	80°F
Saturday	79°F

11. What was the mean high temperature for the week?

A. 80°F
B. 81°F
C. 82°F
D. 83°F

12. What was the median high temperature for the week?

A. 80°F
B. 81°F
C. 82°F
D. 83°F

13. What was the mode high temperature for the week?

A. 80°F
B. 81°F
C. 82°F
D. 83°F

Lesson 13: Probability

Probability is the chance that an event will occur. Probability can be expressed as a fraction, decimal, or percent.

Theoretical Probability

Theoretical probability is based on mathematical reasoning. The following formula can be used to find the probability, P, that an event will occur.

$$P(\text{event}) = \frac{\text{number of favorable outcomes}}{\text{number of possible outcomes}}$$

Probability can be expressed as a fraction or decimal between and including 0 and 1. It also can be expressed as a percent between and including 0% and 100%. If an event is certain to occur, it has a probability of 1 (100%). If it is impossible for an event to occur, it has a probability of 0 (0%).

Simple events

Simple events have only one outcome.

> **Example**
>
> What is the probability of rolling a 3 on a number cube numbered 1 through 6? Express the probability as a fraction, decimal, and percent.
>
> A cube has 6 sides. Each side has a different number on it: 1, 2, 3, 4, 5, or 6. Therefore, the number of possible outcomes is 6. Since each number has an equal chance of being rolled, there is 1 favorable outcome (rolling a 3). The probability is found as follows.
>
> $$P(\text{rolling a 3}) = \frac{\text{number of favorable outcomes}}{\text{number of possible outcomes}} = \frac{1}{6}$$
>
> The probability of rolling a 3 on a number cube is $\frac{1}{6}$. As a decimal, the probability is $0.1\overline{6}$. As a percent, the probability is $16.\overline{6}\%$

 TIP: When probability is expressed as a fraction, it is usually in lowest terms.

Practice

Directions: For Numbers 1 through 4, express each probability as a fraction, decimal, and percent. Round decimals to the nearest thousandth and percents to the nearest tenth.

1. If you guess the answer to a true-or-false question, what is the probability of answering it correctly?

   _____

2. The 26 different letters of the alphabet are written on cards, one letter per card, and the cards are shuffled. If one card is drawn, what is the probability of drawing the card with the letter Q on it?

   _____

3. Each number from 1 through 10 is written on an identical slip of paper and the slips are put into a hat. If one slip of paper is pulled out of the hat, what is the probability of pulling out a slip that has a multiple of 3 on it?

   _____

4. If a number cube numbered 1 through 6 is rolled once, what is the probability of rolling a prime number?

   _____

Directions: Use the following information to find the probabilities for Numbers 5 through 9. Express each probability as a fraction.

David has 27 golf balls in his golf bag: 8 are orange, 3 are yellow, 15 are white, and 1 is pink. He is going to take one golf ball out of his bag without looking.

5. P(orange): _____

6. P(yellow): _____

7. P(white): _____

8. P(blue): _____

9. What is the best prediction for the color of golf ball David will take out of his bag?

   A. pink
   B. white
   C. yellow
   D. orange

Complement of an event

The **complement** of an event consists of all the possible outcomes other than the given event. The complement can be written with the symbol ′ next to the event (read as "not"). The probability that the complement of an event, E′, will occur is equal to 1 minus the probability that the event, E, will occur.

$$P(E') = 1 - P(E)$$

Example

If a number cube numbered 1 through 6 is rolled once, what is the probability of **not rolling a 2**, $P(2')$?

$$P(2') = 1 - P(2)$$

$$= 1 - \frac{1}{6}$$

$$= \frac{5}{6}$$

The probability of not rolling a 2 is $\frac{5}{6}$.

Practice

Directions: Use the following information to find the probabilities for Numbers 1 through 5. Express each probability as a fraction, decimal, and percent.

Myra has a bag that contains the following marbles: 8 red, 1 black, 2 green, 5 blue, and 4 white. Myra is going to pick one marble from the bag without looking.

1. P(**not** picking a red marble): _____

2. P(**not** picking a blue marble): _____

3. P(**not** picking a green marble): _____

4. P(**not** picking a white marble): _____

5. P(**not** picking a black marble): _____

Independent Events

Two or more events that have no influence on each other are **independent**. To find the probability of independent events, multiply the individual probabilities.

Example

Dylan has 6 neckties: one red, one blue, two striped, and two plaid. He has 4 shirts: one white, one blue, and two gray. If Dylan reaches into his closet without looking, what is the probability that he will choose a plaid tie **and** a gray shirt? Express each probability as a fraction.

Step 1: **Find the probability of the first event (P_1).**

$$P_1(\text{plaid tie}): \frac{2}{6} = \frac{1}{3}$$

Step 2: **Find the probability of the second event (P_2).**

$$P_2(\text{gray shirt}): \frac{2}{4} = \frac{1}{2}$$

Step 3: **Multiply P_1 and P_2.**

$$P(\text{plaid tie, gray shirt}): P_1 \bullet P_2 = \frac{1}{3} \bullet \frac{1}{2} = \frac{1}{6}$$

Practice

Directions: Use the information from the example above to answer Numbers 1 through 5. Express each probability as a fraction.

1. What is the probability of choosing a striped tie **and** a gray shirt? _____

2. What is the probability of choosing a red tie **and** a white shirt? _____

3. What is the probability of choosing a blue tie **and** a gray shirt? _____

4. Which event in Numbers 1 through 3 is **most** likely to occur?

   _____

5. Which event in Numbers 1 through 3 is **least** likely to occur?

   _____

Dependent Events

Two or more events that are influenced by each other are **dependent**. The total number of outcomes in the second event is affected by the action that occurs in the first event. To find the probability of dependent events, multiply the individual probabilities.

Example

There are 7 marbles in a pouch: 3 are black and 4 are red. Two are chosen at random and removed, one after the other. What is the probability that the first marble is black and the second marble is red? Express each probability as a fraction. Remember that after the first marble is chosen, there is one less marble in the pouch.

Step 1: **Find the probability of the first event (P_1).**

P_1(black marble): $\frac{3}{7}$

Step 2: **Find the probability of the second event (P_2).**

P_2(red marble): $\frac{4}{6} = \frac{2}{3}$

Step 3: **Multiply P_1 and P_2.**

P(black marble, red marble): $P_1 \bullet P_2 = \frac{3}{7} \bullet \frac{2}{3} = \frac{6}{21} = \frac{2}{7}$

Practice

Directions: Use the following information to answer Numbers 1 and 2. Express each probability as a fraction.

Lorenzo has a jar of seven olives. Two are green and five are black. Two are chosen at random and removed one after the other.

1. What is the probability of choosing a black olive first and a green olive second?

   _____

2. What is the probability of choosing a black olive first and a black olive second?

   _____

Counting Techniques and Probability

There are many different counting techniques that can be used to determine possible outcomes and to calculate probability.

Tree diagrams

A **tree diagram** uses branches to show all possible outcomes of an event.

Example

At Washington High School, each sophomore student is assigned to a gym class based on the following information.

   Day: Tuesday (Tue.) or Thursday (Thurs.)

   Time: A.M. or P.M.

   Place: Gym 1 or Gym 2

What is the probability that a sophomore student will have gym class on Thursday A.M. in Gym 2? The following tree diagram shows that there are 8 possible outcomes for a gym class.

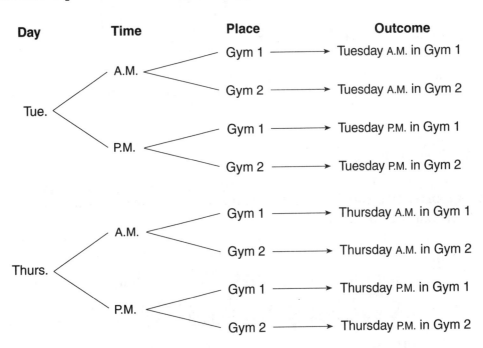

The probability that a sophomore student will have gym class on Thursday A.M. in Gym 2 is $\frac{1}{8}$, 0.125, or 12.5%.

Tables

Sometimes it is helpful to use a table to show all possible outcomes.

Example

Tony is going to roll two number cubes and then find the sum of the two numbers that face upward. What is the probability of getting a sum of 8? Tony made the following table to show that there are 36 possible outcomes.

First Number Cube

Second Number Cube	1	2	3	4	5	6
1	2	3	4	5	6	7
2	3	4	5	6	7	8
3	4	5	6	7	8	9
4	5	6	7	8	9	10
5	6	7	8	9	10	11
6	7	8	9	10	11	12

Since there are 5 different ways to get a sum of 8, the probability is $\frac{5}{36}$.

Organized lists

If you don't like drawing diagrams and tables, you can use a list to show all possible outcomes.

Example

The following list shows the possible outcomes of tossing a coin three times. What is the probability of all three tosses landing heads up? The following list shows that there are 8 possible outcomes.

HHH	HTH	THH	TTH
HHT	HTT	THT	TTT

The probability of all three tosses landing heads up is $\frac{1}{8}$.

Practice

Directions: Use the following information to answer Numbers 1 through 4.

Vince is the coach of the tenth-grade football team. Before each game, he likes to choose the first three offensive plays of the game. For each offensive play of the game, the team can either run the ball or pass the ball.

1. Make a tree diagram to show the different outcomes.

2. What is the probability that the team will run three times? _____

3. What is the probability that the team will run twice and pass once?

_____

4. What is the probability that the team will pass at least once? _____

Directions: Use the following information to answer Numbers 5 through 7.

Kim, Joe, and Steve are the three finalists in a spelling bee. The order in which they will spell in the final round will be determined by a random draw.

5. Make a list to show the different orders in which Kim, Joe, and Steve can spell.

6. What is the probability that Kim will spell second? _____

7. What is the probability that Steve will spell first or second? _____

Directions: Use the following information to answer Numbers 8 and 9.

Jill is going to roll two number cubes and multiply the two numbers that are facing upward. She made the following table to show the possible outcomes.

First Number Cube

	1	2	3	4	5	6
1	1	2	3	4	5	6
2	2	4	6	8	10	12
3	3	6	9	12	15	18
4	4	8	12	16	20	24
5	5	10	15	20	25	30
6	6	12	18	24	30	36

Second Number Cube

8. What is the probability that the product will be 30? _____

9. What is the probability that the product will be 12? _____

Test Your Skills

Directions: Use the following information to answer Numbers 1 and 2.

Mr. Foley's tenth-grade class is in charge of the school store. The following table shows the store's current stock of folders and notebooks.

Color	Folders	Notebooks
Red	3	0
Yellow	2	4
Green	1	3
Blue	4	5
TOTAL	10	12

1. If a student randomly chooses a folder, what color of folder has a 40% chance of being chosen?

   A. red
   B. yellow
   C. green
   D. blue

2. Which pair has zero probability of being sold?

   A. red folder and red notebook
   B. yellow folder and yellow notebook
   C. green folder and green notebook
   D. blue folder and blue notebook

Directions: Use the following information to answer Numbers 3 through 5.

Eighteen marbles are dropped into a jar. There are 8 black marbles, 7 red ones, and 3 silver ones. Marbles are chosen from the jar without looking.

3. If one marble is chosen, what is the probability that it will be **red**?

   A. $0.1\overline{6}$
   B. $0.3\overline{8}$
   C. $0.\overline{4}$
   D. $0.\overline{5}$

4. If one marble is chosen, what is the probability that it will **not** be silver?

   A. $16.\overline{6}\%$
   B. $55.\overline{5}\%$
   C. $61.\overline{1}\%$
   D. $83.\overline{3}\%$

5. If two marbles are chosen without replacing them, what is the probability of choosing a black marble first **and** a silver marble second?

   A. $\frac{2}{27}$

   B. $\frac{4}{51}$

   C. $\frac{11}{18}$

   D. $\frac{95}{153}$

6. Claire is going to toss the following coin and spin the following spinner once.

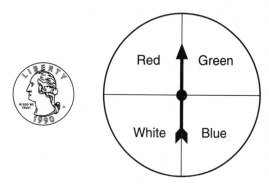

What is the probability that the coin will land tails up **and** the spinner will **not** land on the green section?

A. $\frac{1}{8}$

B. $\frac{1}{4}$

C. $\frac{3}{8}$

D. $\frac{1}{2}$

7. Mrs. Baker has to choose 2 students to lead the class field trip. If she randomly draws from a list of 6 boys and 6 girls, what is the probability that 2 girls will be chosen?

A. $\frac{1}{7}$

B. $\frac{5}{24}$

C. $\frac{5}{22}$

D. $\frac{5}{6}$

8. Jessica is playing a board game that uses the following spinner. When she spins the spinner, she gets to move the number of spaces equal to the number that the spinner lands on.

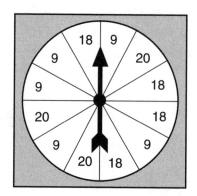

What is the probability that Jessica will get to move 20 spaces on her next turn?

A. $\frac{1}{3}$

B. $\frac{1}{4}$

C. $\frac{1}{5}$

D. $\frac{1}{6}$

9. If a coin is flipped three times, what is the probability of **at least** two heads landing up in the three tosses?

A. $\frac{1}{2}$

B. $\frac{3}{8}$

C. $\frac{1}{4}$

D. $\frac{1}{8}$

CAHSEE Mathematics Blueprint

Buckle Down on CAHSEE Mathematics is based on the content standards of the CAHSEE Mathematics Blueprint adopted by the California State Board of Education. The following table matches the standards with the *Buckle Down* lessons in which they are addressed.

Grade 6—Statistics, Data Analysis, and Probability	*Buckle Down* Lesson(s)
1.0 **Students compute and analyze statistical measurements for data sets:**	
1.1 Compute the mean, median, and mode of data sets.	12
2.0 **Students use data samples of a population and describe the characteristics and limitations of the samples:**	
2.5 Identify claims based on statistical data and, in simple cases, evaluate the validity of the claims.	12
3.0 **Students determine theoretical and experimental probabilities and use these to make predictions about events:**	
3.1 Represent all possible outcomes for compound events in an organized way (e.g., tables, grids, tree diagrams) and express the theoretical probability of each outcome.	13
3.3 Represent probabilities as ratios, proportions, decimals between 0 and 1, and percentages between 0 and 100 and verify that the probabilities computed are reasonable; know that if P is the probability of an event, $1-P$ is the probability of an event not occurring.	13
3.5 Understand the difference between independent and dependent events.	13

Grade 7—Number Sense	*Buckle Down* Lesson(s)
1.0 **Students know the properties of, and compute with, rational numbers expressed in a variety of forms:**	
1.1 Read, write, and compare rational numbers in scientific notation (positive and negative powers of 10) with approximate numbers using scientific notation.	1
1.2 Add, subtract, multiply, and divide rational numbers (integers, fractions, and terminating decimals) and take positive rational numbers to whole-number powers.	1, 2
1.3 Convert fractions to decimals and percents and use these representations in estimations, computations, and applications.	1, 2, 3
1.6 Calculate the percentage of increases and decreases of a quantity.	3
1.7 Solve problems that involve discounts, markups, commissions, and profit and compute simple and compound interest.	3
2.0 **Students use exponents, powers, and roots and use exponents in working with fractions:**	
2.1 Understand negative whole-number exponents. Multiply and divide expressions involving exponents with a common base.	1, 2, 5
2.2 Add and subtract fractions by using factoring to find common denominators.	2
2.3 Multiply, divide, and simplify rational numbers by using exponent rules.	2
2.4 Use the inverse relationship between raising to a power and extracting the root of a perfect square integer; for an integer that is not square, determine without a calculator the two integers between which its square root lies and explain why.	1
2.5 Understand the meaning of the absolute value of a number; interpret the absolute value as the distance of the number from zero on a number line; and determine the absolute value of real numbers.	1, 4

Grade 7—Algebra and Functions	*Buckle Down* Lesson(s)
1.0 **Students express quantitative relationships by using algebraic terminology, expressions, equations, inequalities, and graphs:**	
1.1 Use variables and appropriate operations to write an expression, an equation, an inequality, or a system of equations or inequalities that represents a verbal description (e.g., three less than a number, half as large as area *A*).	4, 5, 7
1.2 Use the correct order of operations to evaluate algebraic expressions such as $3(2x + 5)^2$.	4, 5
1.5 Represent quantitative relationships graphically and interpret the meaning of a specific part of a graph in the situation represented by the graph.	4, 6, 7, 8, 12
2.0 **Students interpret and evaluate expressions involving integer powers and simple roots:**	
2.1 Interpret positive whole-number powers as repeated multiplication and negative whole-number powers as repeated division or multiplication by the multiplicative inverse. Simplify and evaluate expressions that include exponents.	5
2.2 Multiply and divide monomials; extend the process of taking powers and extracting roots to monomials when the latter results in a monomial with an integer exponent.	5
3.0 **Students graph and interpret linear and some nonlinear functions:**	
3.1 Graph functions of the form $y = nx^2$ and $y = nx^3$ and use in solving problems.	8
3.3 Graph linear functions, noting that the vertical change (change in *y*-value) per unit of horizontal change (change in *x*-value) is always the same and know that the ratio ("rise over run") is called the slope of a graph.	6
3.4 Plot the values of quantities whose ratios are always the same (e.g., cost to the number of an item, feet to inches, circumference to diameter of a circle). Fit a line to the plot and understand that the slope of a line equals the quantities.	6
4.0 **Students solve simple linear equations and inequalities over the rational numbers:**	
4.1 Solve two-step linear equations and inequalities in one variable over the rational numbers, interpret the solution or solutions in the context from which they arose, and verify the reasonableness of the results.	4
4.2 Solve multistep problems involving rate, average speed, distance, and time or a direct variation.	4

Grade 7—Measurement and Geometry	*Buckle Down* Lesson(s)
1.0 Students choose appropriate units of measure and use ratios to convert within and between measurement systems to solve problems:	
1.1 Compare weights, capacities, geometric measures, times, and temperatures within and between measurement systems (e.g., miles per hour and feet per second, cubic inches to cubic centimeters).	9, 10
1.2 Construct and read drawings and models made to scale.	9
1.3 Use measures expressed as rates (e.g., speed, density) and measures expressed as products (e.g., person-days) to solve problems; check the units of the solutions; and use dimensional analysis to check the reasonableness of the answer.	4, 9
2.0 Students compute the perimeter, area, and volume of common geometric objects and use the results to find measures of less common objects. They know how perimeter, area and volume are affected by changes of scale:	
2.1 Use formulas routinely for finding the perimeter and area of basic two-dimensional figures and the surface area and volume of basic three-dimensional figures, including rectangles, parallelograms, trapezoids, squares, triangles, circles, prisms and cylinders.	10
2.2 Estimate and compute the area of more complex or irregular two- and three-dimensional figures by breaking the figures down into more basic geometric objects.	10
2.3 Compute the length of the perimeter, the surface area of the faces, and the volume of a three-dimensional object built from rectangular solids. Understand that when the lengths of all dimensions are multiplied by a scale factor, the surface area is multiplied by the square of the scale factor and volume is multiplied by the cube of the scale factor.	10
2.4 Relate the changes in measurement with a change of scale to the units used (e.g., square inches, cubic feet) and to conversions between units (1 square foot = 144 square inches or [1 ft^2] = [144 in^2], 1 cubic inch is approximately 16.38 cubic centimeters or [1 in^3] = [16.38 cm^3].)	9, 10

		Buckle Down Lesson(s)
Grade 7—Measurement and Geometry *(Continued)*		
3.0	**Students know the Pythagorean theorem and deepen their understanding of plane and solid geometric shapes by constructing figures that meet given conditions and by identifying attributes of figures:**	
	3.2 Understand and use coordinate graphs to plot simple figures, determine lengths and areas related to them, and determine their image under translations and reflections.	11
	3.3 Know and understand the Pythagorean theorem and its converse and use it to find the length of the missing side of a right triangle and the lengths of other line segments and, in some situations, empirically verify the Pythagorean theorem by direct measurement.	11
	3.4 Demonstrate an understanding of conditions that indicate two geometrical figures are congruent and what congruence means about the relationships between the sides and angles of the two figures.	11
Grade 7—Statistics, Data Analysis, and Probability		
1.0	**Students collect, organize, and represent data sets that have one or more variables and identify relationships among variables within a data set by hand and through the use of an electronic spreadsheet software program:**	
	1.1 Know various forms of display for data sets; use the forms to display a single set of data or to compare two sets of data.	12
	1.2 Represent two numerical variables on a scatterplot and informally describe how the data points are distributed and any apparent relationship that exists between the two variables (e.g., between time spent on homework and grade level).	12
Grade 7—Mathematical Reasoning		
1.0	**Students make decisions about how to approach problems:**	
	1.1 Analyze problems by identifying relationships, distinguishing relevant from irrelevant information, identifying missing information, sequencing and prioritizing information, and observing patterns.	1–13
	1.2 Formulate and justify mathematical conjectures based on a general description of the mathematical question or problem posed.	1–13

Grade 7—Mathematical Reasoning *(Continued)*	*Buckle Down* Lesson(s)
2.0 **Student use strategies, skills, and concepts in finding solutions:**	
2.1 Use estimation to verify the reasonableness of calculated results.	1–13
2.3 Estimate unknown quantities graphically and solve for them by using logical reasoning and arithmetic and algebraic techniques.	6, 7, 8, 12
2.4 Make and test conjectures by using both inductive and deductive reasoning.	1–13
3.0 **Students determine a solution is complete and move beyond a particular problem by generalizing to other situations:**	
3.3 Develop generalizations of the results obtained and the strategies used and apply them to new problem situations.	1–13
Algebra I	
2.0 **Students understand and use such operations as taking the opposite, finding the reciprocal, and taking a root. They understand and use the rules of exponents.**	1, 2, 4, 5
3.0 **Students solve equations and inequalities involving absolute values.**	4
4.0 **Students simplify expressions before solving linear equations and inequalities in one variable, such as $3(2x - 5) + 4(x - 2) = 12$.**	4
5.0 **Students solve multistep problems, including word problems, involving linear equations and linear inequalities in one variable and provide justification for each step.**	4
6.0 **Students graph a linear equation and compute the x- and y-intercepts (e.g., graph $2x + 6y = 4$).**	6
7.0 **Students verify that a point lies on a line, given an equation of the line. Students are able to derive linear equations.**	6
8.0 **Students understand the concepts of parallel lines and how their slopes are related.**	6
9.0 **Students solve a system of two linear equations in two variables algebraically and are able to interpret the answer graphically. Students are able to solve a system of two linear inequalities in two variables and to sketch the solution sets.**	7
10.0 **Students add, subtract, multiply, and divide monomials and polynomials. Students solve multistep problems, including word problems, by using these techniques.**	5
15.0 **Students apply algebraic techniques to solve rate problems, work problems, and percent mixture problems.**	4